BEAUTY
IN
BLACK PERFORMANCE

PLAYS FOR AFRICAN AMERICAN YOUTH

BY
CAROLYN NUR WISTRAND

Africa World Press, Inc.

P.O. Box 1892  P.O. Box 48
Trenton, NJ 08607   Asmara, ERITREA

Africa World Press, Inc.

P.O. Box 1892
Trenton, NJ 08607

P.O. Box 48
Asmara, ERITREA

Book design: Saverance Publishing Services
Cover design: Dapo Ojo-Ade
Photographs by Rosalie Howell

Library of Congress Cataloging-in-Publication Data

Wistrand, Carolyn Nur.
  Beauty in Black performance : plays for African American youth / by Carolyn Nur Wistrand.
    p. cm.
  ISBN 1-59221-379-0 -- ISBN 1-59221-380-4 (pbk.)
  1. Young adult drama, American. 2. African Americans--History--Drama. 3. Blacks--Drama. I. Title.

PS3623.I848B43 2006
812'.6--dc22

                      2005033213

FOREWORD

I'll admit it: I was once ashamed of being black. Brought up as one of nine children to parents who had fled rural Virginia as part of the continuing migration of disenfranchised African-Americans, determined to escape the fear and claustrophobia of bigotry, they ended up in a small community 14 miles north of the city of Philadelphia along with other blacks from a wide spectrum of the South — North and South Carolina, Texas, Georgia, Florida, Alabama, Mississippi, and Tennessee. Instead of the Promised Land they were seeking, they were met as intruders, whose crude, self-built homes were met with derisive laughter from whites who rode or walked by and referred to as "tar paper houses." In truth, eleven of us — nine children and my parents — lived in the cellar of a house that was being hastily constructed by my father. The wood flooring of the first floor was covered over by tar paper as protection from inclement weather. The cellar floor was comprised of dirt and we lived primitively, besieged by the heat of summer and the cold, sweeping gusts of winter winds. We slept on pallets made of straw imbedded in burlap and were made even more uncomfortable by a defective coal stove that spewed as much smoke as it did heat. The fact that others in our community were living in much the same manner was not assuaging. We were not as our parents, who steeled themselves against ridicule and racist taunts, knowing that there would be better days ahead, knowing that it wasn't always going to be that way. We were embarrassed — humiliated.

This same humiliation was reinforced on the very first day of school in a township that had had very little contact with Blacks, nor did it wish to. When my sister and I appeared at the door of our 4th grade class room (I couldn't attend school for an entire year because I had suffered a debilitating bone disease and almost died), we were greeted by a teacher who panicked when she saw us and scurried to the door where we tentatively stood, flinging over her shoulder an admonishment to the members of the class, "All right now, don't be afraid of the natives now! Don't be afraid of the natives!" Even though I and the other few blacks attending the school later distinguished ourselves either academically or athletically, our experiences were fraught with attempts to break our spirits and our will. We didn't bend, but it was scarring, damaging, and reached its apex when my eleventh grade English teacher refused to believe that I had written a short story and wouldn't accept it. She chastised me publicly and demanded that I rewrite it, which meant that I was to somehow dumb it down. To be black, in essence, for me, was to be ashamed of it. It meant a rejection of my own mother and father, and family, whatever history they had brought along with them. I struck out on my own. I went on a journey, no longer in need of a past, seeking only a future that excluded family, friends, and religion. I drifted, seeking truths that were separate from the ones I had known. I began to flounder. I became a man with no history or roots. I was in the middle of an ocean in a boat without oars or a rudder. I felt lost, alone, tired of living a life without history, family and religion, and one day I rushed home to that small community that and shaped and honed me, and I sat down beside my mother and begged her to "tell me about my past. And from her I learned her parents had been sharecroppers. And their parents had also been sharecroppers, and those before them had been slaves and descendants of slaves. They had been the backbone of this country and had died ingloriously, forgotten and buried under giant, ignominious mounds of time. It was these people and their efforts to pave the way for me that I had disrespected in rejecting my past. I know better now. We are all past, present, and future. We are the souls and spirits of those who have come before us. Carolyn Nur Wistrand clearly emphasizes and reinforces this in each of her literary efforts. Her vivid characters, the imagery and power that emanates from them, are prisms in which African Americans can see, feel, hear, touch and taste the past and recognize its travesties but also its inherent beauties. Her passion and intellect serve not only to inform us, but to help us discover more about the rhythms, music and dialogue of days long past — days, however, that still resonate in the present and serve as a beacon to the future. She is a curator and caretaker of history. In this work as she has in all of her efforts, she has allowed us to enter into it as a participant and not simply as a spectator. We do not have to any longer, ride the sea alone in a craft without oars and a rudder. Thank you, Carolyn.

-Leslie Lee

PLAYS IN THIS VOLUME

Ida B. 'n The Lynching Tree
A Record of Race History
Dramatized for the stage by Carolyn Nur Wistrand

The play moves swiftly through the major events in the life of Miss Ida B. Wells, from her birth on July 16, 1862 in Holly Springs, Mississippi to the Memphis lynchings of March 9, 1892, which resulted in her lifelong crusade against lynching and inequities brought about by Jim Crow.

PAGEANT ONE	PAGEANT TWO	PAGEANT THREE	PAGEANT FOUR
Honoring Ida's Ancestors	*Ida B. Wells becomes a school-teacher and sues the railroad*	*The Memphis Lynchings*	*Crusade for Justice*
Elderly Ida	Elderly Ida	Elderly Ida	Elderly Ida
Ida B. Wells	Ida B. Wells	Ida B. Wells	Ida B. Wells
Journalists	Eugenia	Journalists	Reverend
Miss Polly	Masons	Mrs. Washington	Townspeople
Miss Peggy	Conductor	Mrs. Jefferson	Criminal Judge
James Wells	Reverend	Headmistress	Journalists
Elizabeth Wells	Crowd on Beale Street	Tommie Moss	Crowd
Preacher	Robert. R. Church	Betty Moss	
Sistah Jefferson	Nathan Bedford Forrest	Calvin McDowell	
Brotha Jefferson	Headmistress	Henry Stewart	
Congregation	Passengers on Train	Dora	
White Missionary	Porter	Willa Mae	
Ku Klux Klan	Journalists	Reverend	
Young Ida (Ida B. Wells)	Judge Pierce	Grand Dragon	
Grandma Peggy		Ku Klux Klan	
Masons		Sheriff	
		Townspeople	

PAGEANT ONE
Honoring Ida's Ancestors

Chicago, Illinois. 1930.

An elderly Ida B. Wells-Barnett is seated at her Victorian writing desk. An elegant woman of color in her early sixties, her appearance at once evokes the impression of a stately and noble woman.

ELDERLY IDA

To keep the waters troubled ...was to be awake while others slept. No sweet dreams brought me peace, knowing justice as a marble statue that heard not the cries from the lynching tree. "Perhaps my work will be forgotten…perhaps America will write a different history…but youth…our youth are entitled to the facts of race history, which only the participants can give, I am thus led to set forth the facts." *(Opening her manuscript she dips her pen in the inkwell, and begins to write.)* I was born in Holly Springs, Mississippi, July 16, 1862. It was in the midst of the great Civil War.

A male journalist runs in.

JOURNALIST

Get this on the press!

Additional journalists dash in with clipboards, writing furiously.

JOURNALIST

July 16, 1862.

JOURNALIST

President Lincoln announced today the Union army suffered a major loss at the battle of Bull Run. Confederates have pushed Union soldiers out of Virginia. STOP.

Young Ida B. Wells enters in a floor length dark skirt and long white Victorian blouse, her hair piled elegantly in the fashion of the 1890's. She moves to the center platform as the journalists surround her, recording the facts of her life.

IDA B. WELLS

I was born to James Wells.

JOURNALIST

Age of your father?

IDA B. WELLS

Twenty-one. A mulatto slave born in Tippah County, Mississippi.

JOURNALIST

Mulatto?

IDA B. WELLS

He was the son of his white master.

JOURNALIST

Your father had white brothers and sisters?

IDA B. WELLS

His master had no children by his wife.

Miss Polly, a white woman dressed as a plantation wife and Miss Peggy, a black woman dressed as a plantation slave appear.

MISS POLLY

(*Fanning herself*) I tried to give him children. Five of them. Stillborn.

JOURNALIST

So your grandmother had children by her master?

MISS PEGGY

Mastah called for me…I wanted to die.

MISS POLLY

I wished ya would have died. Your belly full with my husband's seed.

MISS PEGGY

You got your revenge, Miss Polly…day he die.

MISS POLLY

Bring her over here! Her and those pickaninies. Beat her. Bad. 'Til the blood runs down her feet.

Miss Peggy and Miss Polly swiftly exit.

JOURNALIST

Your mother?

IDA B. WELLS

My mother was Elizabeth Warrenton.

JOURNALIST

Age?

IDA B. WELLS

Mother was eighteen. A Negress slave from Virginia.

JOURNALIST

Your father's work?

IDA B. WELLS

He was a carpenter. His master/father hired him out to a Mr. Bolling in Holly Springs.

JOURNALIST

What was your mother's work?

IDA B. WELLS

She was a cook in the Bolling household.

JOURNALIST

Were they married?

IDA B. WELLS

They were slaves.

JOURNALIST

Please answer the question.

IDA B. WELLS

Slaves were not allowed to obtain a legal marriage. Remember, the Constitution did not guarantee their freedom. They lived as man and wife.

Ida leaves as the journalists rapidly change positions.

JOURNALIST

Get this on the press!

JOURNALIST

January 1, 1863. Washington D.C.

JOURNALIST

Pittsburgh, Pennsylvania.

JOURNALIST

Richmond, Virginia.

JOURNALIST

Chicago, Illinois.

JOURNALIST

Charlotte, North Carolina.

JOURNALIST

Detroit, Michigan.

JOURNALIST

Memphis, Tennessee.

JOURNALIST

President Lincoln has signed into law today, the Emancipation Proclamation. Slavery has been abolished. STOP.

Journalists are motionless as Jim Wells runs onstage with a newspaper.

JIM WELLS

Lizzie! Where are ya? Elizabeth Wells!

Elizabeth Wells runs in with a baby in her arms.

ELIZABETH WELLS

What wrong?

JIM WELLS

What right is the Word of God when Moses told Pharaoh, "Let my people go!"

ELIZABETH WELLS

Why you so excited, Jim Wells?

JIM WELLS

Cause 'a this newspaper is what Ah'm talkin' about! Here it is on the headline page in the Memphis Star. *(Reading)* LINCOLN DECLARES SLAVERY UNCONSTITUIONAL.

ELIZABETH WELLS

Unconstitutional?

JIM WELLS

Freedom.

ELIZABETH WELLS

Hush your mouth.

JIM WELLS

God as my witness. Jim Wells a free man.

ELIZABETH WELLS

Someone gone hear you!

JIM WELLS

Bring Ida B. over here.

ELIZABETH WELLS

There still a war.

JIM WELLS

These our walkin' papers. God has heard the cry of our people.

ELIZABETH WELLS

Slave or free…you a righteous man, Jim Wells.

JIM WELLS

We gone have a legal wedding…day this war ends.

Jim and Elizabeth exit as journalists come to life.

JOURNALIST

Get this on the press!

JOURNALIST

April 9, 1865. Appomattox Court House, Virginia.

JOURNALIST

LEE SURRENDERS TO GRANT!

JOURNALIST

General Robert E. Lee surrendered the Confederate Army to Lieutenant General Ulysses S. Grant in the town of Appomattox, Court House, Virginia, at approximately 2 PM today, April 9, 1865.

JOURNALIST

The Civil War has ended. STOP.

Humming of a congregation is heard as journalists depart and Preacher, Jim Wells, Elizabeth Wells, and congregation enter.

PREACHER

Do you James Wells, take Elizabeth Warrenton, to be your lawful wedded wife, to have and to hold, in sickness and in health, 'til death do you part?

JIM WELLS

I do.

PREACHER

Do you, Elizabeth Warrenton, take James Wells to be your lawful wedded husband, to have and to hold, in sickness and in health, 'til death do you part?

ELIZABETH

I do.

PREACHER

By the powers vested in me, by the Spirit of God, and the law of this land, I now pronounce you man and wife. Let no man tear asunder what God hath joined.

Congregation breaks out in song, "This Little Light of Mine", Southern Gospel style. James and Elizabeth join the singing, dancing congregation. Preacher steps up to the pulpit as the congregation chants a call and response to the sermon.

PREACHER

To know the laws of God you got to read the Holy Book!

CONGREGATION

Read the Holy Book!

PREACHER

Lord God gave you everything you need in this world. To know His Ways, you got to read His Words!

CONGREGATION

Amen!

PREACHER

This is a great day in Mississippi. I say! This is a great day in Holly Springs, Mississippi. Tomorrow morning, Monday morning, they open the doors at Shaw University, where every Black man, and every Black woman, and every Black child gone be welcome.

Sistah Jefferson jumps up. Brotha Jefferson stands with her.

SISTAH JEFFERSON

I was stripped and beaten for trying to read the holy book.

PREACHER

You gotta let that go, Sistah Jefferson. This a new day!

CONGREGATION

New day!

PREACHER

I'M COMING DOWN THERE SISTAH!

WOMAN FROM CONGREGATION

Take your time, Preacher!

PREACHER

You gonna fill your woman with the holy seed of life?

BROTHA JEFFERSON
    She with child, Preacher.

PREACHER
    God as my witness that child will read the holy book! Can you read, Sistah Jefferson?

SISTAH JEFFERSON
    Afraid to read is what Ah'ma telling ya!

PREACHER
    Brotha Jefferson?

BROTHA JEFFERSON
    I try to tell her the war over, Preacher!

PREACHER
    I want every man and woman who can read to come up here.

    Jim Wells walks up to Preacher.

JIM WELLS
    I can read the holy book, Preacher. When that door open tomorrow at Shaw University, my wife walking in there, Ida B. sucking from her milk.

PREACHER
    You a righteous man, Jim Wells!

CONGREGATION
    Righteous man!

PREACHER
    Jim Wells, what you got to say to Sistah Jefferson?

JIM WELLS
    Ain't no white man gone come in that school to beat ya.

CONGREGATION
    Ah knows that's right!

JIM WELLS
    You go over there with my wife, Lizzie, she sit with ya.

PREACHER
    1865! And it's a new day in Mississippi! I'm expecting, I say! I'm expecting every Mother God blessed with the seed of life to be sitting in Shaw University with their childrens come Monday morning. Cause it's a new day in Mississippi.

CONGREGATION
    A NEW DAY IN MISSISSIPPI!

    Female members of congregation become the students of Shaw University. The Preacher exits with the men as a Northern White female missionary assumes the position of teacher.

ELDERLY IDA

And when the people walked into Shaw University, they say something they had never seen in Mississippi. A Northern missionary, spirit filled.

MISSIONARY

"He brought me to the gate, the gate facing east. And behold, The glory of the God of Israel came from the east; and the sound of His coming was like the sound of many waters."

STUDENTS

(Reading in unison) "The sound of His coming was like the sound of many waters."

MISSIONARY

"As the glory of the Lord entered the temple by the gate facing East."

STUDENTS

"As the glory of the Lord entered the temple by the gate facing East."

MISSIONARY

Elizabeth Wells.

Elizabeth Wells rises and reads from the Bible.

ELIZABETH WELLS

"And the earth shone with his glory."

MISSIONARY

Sister Jefferson.

SISTAH JEFFERSON

"And the earth shone with his glory."

MISSIONARY

Class.

CLASS

"And the earth shone with his glory."

Hooded Klan members strut in and surround the classroom.

KLAN MEMBER

This beat all. Coons sittin' in the Senate 'cause of them Union bastards. But right here, in Holly Springs, niggers learning to read!

MISSIONARY

What is it you want?

KLAN MEMBER

Like these darkies, huh? Couldn't wait to get down here, close enough to smell 'em.

KLAN MEMBER

Smell just like 'em, nigger teacher!

MISSIONARY

You cover your face to call me these things?

KLAN MEMBER
Ain't ya got no people up North to teach?

KLAN MEMBER
Mississippi belongs to the White man. You understand me?

MISSIONARY
You do not intimidate me.

KLAN MEMBER
You ain't welcome down here.

MISSIONARY
My work does not depend on your good will.

KLAN MEMBER
Ya got no protection!

MISSIONARY
God is my protection!

Klan members strut downstage pronouncing.

KLAN
God rules through the White man in Mississippi!

Klan are motionless as Elderly Ida leaves her Victorian writing table and intermingles with the women.

ELDERLY IDA
(Directly to audience) Make no mistake what the South was during Reconstruction. The Black race was no longer the slave.

CLASS
Who gone pick your cotton?

CLASS
Who gone shine your shoes?

CLASS
Who gone plant your rice fields?

CLASS
Who gone cook your food?

ELDERLY IDA
It was a time of growth for our people as the angry White South gave birth to the Ku Klux Klan.

KLAN
The White man will rule in Mississippi! *(Klan exit.)*

CLASS
1878.

ELDERLY IDA

How our family had grown.

MISSIONARY

The trustees of Shaw University do hereby present this Certificate for Perfect Attendance to Mrs. Elizabeth Wells. Awarded this first day of June in the year of our Lord, 1878.

Class claps as Elizabeth Wells come forward to receive her certificate.

MISSIONARY

And now for Academic Achievement. The Board of Trustees of Shaw University is proud to present the Dean's Honor Award to Miss Ida B. Wells.

IDA B. WELLS

Thank you, Sister.

MISSIONARY

You are capable of the advanced college program in September, Miss Wells.

ELIZABETH WELLS

She be at her grannies in September, sister…she be back by winter.

MISSIONARY

Remember your lessons, Miss Wells.

IDA B. WELLS

Yes Ma'am.

The class rapidly disperses as journalists run in. Immediate sense of illness; women cover bodies with white sheets and nurse the sick. Elizabeth Wells lays on center platform, Sistah Jefferson and Missionary nurse her.

JOURNALIST

Get this on the Press! September, 1878.

JOURNALIST

Yellow fever in Memphis!

JOURNALIST

Yellow fever in New Orleans!

JOURNALIST

Yellow fever in Greenville!

JOURNALIST

Fifty cases of yellow fever reported in Grenada, Mississippi. An epidemic of yellow fever has spread throughout the Mississippi Valley. Hundreds are reported dead.

JOURNALIST

Mobile, Alabama. This yellow scourge has come upon the city showing no mercy on our citizens. Mayors of Memphis, New Orleans, Mobile issue quarantine.

JOURNALIST

Yellow fever spreads to Holly Springs!

JOURNALIST
   STOP!

Citizens of Holly Springs enter with cloths tied over their faces. Journalists try to hold the people back.

JOURNALIST
   Ya'll go back right now! That part of the city is under quarantine by the Mayor.

WOMAN
   We go back we gone catch it. They droppin' by the side of the road back there.

JOURNALIST
   How many down with it?

WOMAN
   Least a hundred.

WOMAN
   More like two hundred.

Jim Wells comes running through the crowd.

JIM WELLS
   Excuse me!

WOMAN
   Ain't nothing you can do, Jim Wells.

JIM WELLS
   She need food!

WOMAN
   She can't touch food.

MAN
   Don't go in there!

JIM WELLS
   That's my wife in there!

WOMAN
   Sistah Jefferson nursin' her.

MAN
   Best bleed her you go in there.

JIM WELLS
   Ah knows what I gots to do.

Slow steady movement of people stricken with illness as the humming of "Swing Low, Sweet Chariot" comes up. Elizabeth Wells lies shivering as Sistah Jefferson changes the rags on her head.

JIM WELLS
   How is she?

SISTAH JEFFERSON

Burnin' up.

ELIZABETH WELLS

(*Barely conscious*) Jim...that you?

Sistah Jefferson and attendant bleed Elizabeth's wrists.

JIM WELLS

You got to hold on, Lizzie. (*He dry heaves.*)

SISTAH JEFFERSON

You shouldn't want to see her like this.

JIM WELLS

(*Visibly shaken*) Go on, Sistah. Tend to the others. I'll stay with my wife.

SISTAH JEFFERSON

You gone die with her?

JIM WELLS

If that be the Will of God.

Sound of humming begins to resonate through the crowd.

ELIZABETH WELLS

Jim Wells, you a righteous man.

JIM WELLS

Hold on, Lizzie. Hold on to me.

A lone voice soulfully sings, "Swing Low, Sweet Chariot." Jim Wells drops down by his wife. Sistah Jefferson covers their bodies with a white sheet. Other bodies are covered, until the whole stage is little more than a graveyard. With great dignity the journalists come forward as the mournful humming continues.

JOURNALIST

The stores are all closed. Physicians are broken down.

JOURNALIST

Gloom, despair, and death rule the hour. Only a few have escaped the fever.

JOURNALIST

September 26, 1878.

JOURNALIST

Holly Springs, Mississippi.

Ensemble clears the playing area as Young Ida comes forward and sits on steps. Grandmother Peggy enters and begins sweeping the floor.

IDA B. WELLS

You think Daddy took them to the country?

GRANDMA PEGGY

Haven't heard different.

IDA B. WELLS

Three men entered my grandmother's house.

MAN 1

Miss Peggy?

GRANDMA PEGGY

Over here.

MAN 2

We got a letter from Holly Springs.

IDA B. WELLS

I prayed mother and father were safe from the fever.

GRANDMA PEGGY

Thank you.

Grandma Peggy slowly opens the letter as Ida stands by her side.

GRANDMA PEGGY

Jim and Elizabeth Wells have both died of the fever. Send word to Ida.

Ida collapses. Jim and Elizabeth Wells come forth from the other side.

JIM WELLS

Ida B!

IDA B. WELLS

(*Running toward the voice*) Daddy!

JIM WELLS

Don't come over here.

IDA B. WELLS

Where's Mama?

ELIZABETH WELLS

Right here, baby.

IDA B. WELLS

Who's that?

ELIZABETH WELLS

Baby Stanley.

IDA B. WELLS

He dead?

ELIZABETH WELLS

Yes, baby. Passed over wid your Daddy and me.

JIM WELLS

You in charge now, Ida B.

IDA B. WELLS

Yes, sir.

JIM WELLS

Go back to Holly Springs.

ELIZABETH WELLS

I want to hear nothin' but the Word of God in my house on Sunday.

Jim and Elizabeth Wells begin to walk out of her view.

JIM WELLS

You look after your people.

IDA B. WELLS

Yes, sir.

ELIZABETH WELLS

Only one a my childrens born a slave.

JIM WELLS

You look out for all your people.

Jim and Elizabeth Wells leave from her presence.

ELDERLY IDA

And I say in this year of our Lord, 1930, that James and Elizabeth Wells were righteous people. And I loved them, dearly.

Elderly Ida turns the page of her manuscript and begins a new chapter.

PAGEANT TWO
Ida B. Wells Becomes a Teacher and Sues the Railroad

Ida's crippled sister Eugenia walks into the room as the three men turn to Grandma Peggy.

GRANDMA PEGGY

Ida B.!

IDA B. WELLS

Here I come.

GRANDMA PEGGY

These mens got somethin' to say.

MASON 1

We Masons, just like your father was.

MASON 2

Jim Wells was the best of our race here in Holly Springs. Be proud you carryin' his blood.

MASON 3

> We here to do what's right by him.

MASON 1

> Now Carl's wife here say she take the two youngest girls.

MASON 3

> Both your brothers carpenters…I can use 'em.

MASON 2

> You can look after yourself. This crippled one have to go to the poorhouse. Hate to send her, but that the way it is.

IDA B. WELLS

> Eugenia? Send her to the poorhouse, cause she crippled?

MASON 1

> She can't work.

MASON 2

> Nobody can take on an extra mouth to feed.

IDA B. WELLS

> My parents would turn over in their grave knowin' you farmed us out.

MASON 2

> We trying to do what right by 'em.

IDA B. WELLS

> I'll do what's right by my people. That mean all of us together.

MASON 3

> You still a youngster.

IDA B. WELLS

> Sixteen years is old enough to take care of my own. Will you help me?

The three men walk away and consult for a moment.

MASON 1

> This your father's house.

IDA B. WELLS

> Paid for?

MASON 1

> It's paid for.

IDA B. WELLS

> Did my father have any savings?

MASON 2

> Three hundred dollars.

IDA B. WELLS

That's enough to get us by 'til I pass the examination.

MASON 1

Examination?

IDA B. WELLS

Teacher's Examination for the primary grades.

MASON 1

Theres a cookin' and a cleanin' to take care of.

MASON 2

Who gone take care of the crippled one while you teaching?

GRANDMA PEGGY

Between the two of us…we'll get by.

MASON 1

Alright then, it's settled. *(The men leave.)*

EUGENIA

Are they gonna send me away, Ida?

IDA B. WELLS

You stayin' right here with Grannie and me.

GRANDMA PEGGY

Come over here, chile, so we can let that dress down. You gone be a school teacher.

EUGENIA

Can you pass that test, Ida?

IDA B. WELLS

I guess I can.

EUGENIA

(Studying Ida's appearance to determine what it lacks.) All the school teachers put their hair on top of their heads.

GRANDMA PEGGY

That hairs gots to go up!

Grandma Peggy sticks pins in Ida's hair to make a bun.

EUGENIA

Now you startin' to look like Miss Hopper.

ELDERLY IDA

And I was. At the age of sixteen I became a school teacher. I kept the family together for three years teaching in one of them one room country schools. Grannie had a stroke and Eugenia passed. Nothing left for me in Holly Springs after 1881.

Ida runs off to begin a new chapter of her life.

CONDUCTOR

Welcome to Memphis! Home of Beale Street!

CROWD

(Crowd saunters in) Where the Blues were born!

Memphis Blues comes up and the entire crowd performs a Backwater Blues fast tempo dance number, until Preacher stops the revelry with:

PREACHER

Home of Beale Street Baptist Church what you all need to be thinkin' about!

ROBERT R. CHURCH

Home of Robert R. Church. First Black millionare in Memphis. Made my money in real estate after the yellow fever. I was respected by the good White people of Memphis.

Hooded Klan Man enters.

NATHAN BEDFORD FORREST

You wasn't respected by me! Nathan Bedford Forrest the name. Made my money as a a Memphis slave trader. Those were the days of glory for the white man in Memphis. I'm also proud to tell ya I was the Confederate General that led a massacre on black troops.

ROBERT R. CHURCH

Why you wearing that hood, Forrest?

NATHAN BEDFORD FORREST

Cause I just founded the Ku Klux Klan. The White man will rule in Memphis!

CROWD

White man ain't rulin' on Beale Street!

NATHAN BEDFORD FORREST

Reconstruction over. It's 1881. Civil Rights laws are being repealed right now, in every Southern state.

CROWD

Take it outa here!

NATHAN BEDFORD FORREST

You ever heard a Jim Crow? You about to! *(Quickly exiting)*

Crowd creates a busy street scene as Ida appears, wearing a large straw hat and carrying a suitcase. A young man runs in with a single chair as the Headmistress appears with a clipboard.

HEADMISTRESS

Ida B. Wells!

Ida sits upright in chair. The crowd poses as a background street scene.

IDA B. WELLS

Yes, Ma'am.

HEADMISTRESS

This is an excellent score for a colored girl. Where did you learn such a command of English?

IDA B. WELLS

Shaw University in Holly Springs.

HEADMISTRESS

You will be assigned to the school in Woodstock.

IDA B. WELLS

I was hoping to get on in a school here in Memphis.

HEADMISTRESS

All in good time, Miss Wells. Of course, you will have to take the city examination.

IDA B. WELLS

Yes Ma'am.

HEADMISTRESS

Well, these scores are good enough for our country colored schools. If you are determined to represent the Memphis School Board in public education, you must pass the Memphis School Examination.

IDA B. WELLS

I am determined to do just that.

HEADMISTRESS

Excellent. Now, the pay for the country teacher position is twenty-eight dollars a month. You will begin your assignment on Monday.

IDA B. WELLS

(Standing and facing the Headmistress.) What about books?

Crowd makes an immediate change in pose.

HEADMISTRESS

Books?

IDA B. WELLS

For the children.

HEADMISTRESS

Whatever is available, Miss Wells.

IDA B. WELLS

The country school outside of Holly Springs didn't have books.

HEADMISTRESS

So what did you do?

IDA B. WELLS

I would copy Bible verses.

HEADMISTRESS

Very good, Miss Wells. That will be all. Miss Jackson!

Ida walks away; crowd comes to life.

HEADMISTRESS

Oh, Miss Wells!

Ida and crowd halt.

IDA B. WELLS

Ma'am?

HEADMISTRESS

You will need to take the Chesapeake & Ohio to Woodstock.

IDA B. WELLS

Does the train run everyday?

HEADMISTRESS

You can count on the railroad, Miss Wells.

Conductor rushes in calling out:

CONDUCTOR

All Aboard! All Aboard!
Crowd quickly assembles two railroad cars out of chairs. The rear car is filled with men smoking cigars and pipes. The front car stands empty as women form two lines to gain admittance into the Ladies Car.

CONDUCTOR

Welcome to the Chesapeake & Ohio serving the South from Tennessee to California. Connections in Knoxville take our passengers straight up to New York City. This here the Ladies Car. (*Conductor bows to the 2 White women, as they sit down. He puts his hand up refusing to let the Black women enter the Ladies Car.*) Sometimes we let the Colored women sit up here, sometimes we don't. Back there you got the Smoking car. Cigars, pipes, and cigarettes, every kind of man sits back there when they need to puff.

WHITE WOMAN

No decent White woman would ever ride in a Smoking car!

BLACK WOMAN

No decent Black woman should have ever been made to ride in a Smoking car!

BLACK WOMEN

I know that's right.

Black woman with baby in blanket comes forward. Ida stands next in line.

MISS ADDIE

Excuse me, this is Senator Danfield's child.

CONDUCTOR

Colored or not, that will get you into the Ladies car. This way. (*Miss Addie and Ida enter Ladies car.*) Rest of you need to get on back to the Smoking car.

Black women reluctantly move into the Smoking car, covering their faces with handkerchiefs. Immediate impression of being packed in like rats between men puffing on cigars.

MISS LYLE

Conductor. I have a first class ticket.

CONDUCTOR

And I have a job to do.

MISS LYLE

The Smoking car does not provide first class accommodations.

CONDUCTOR

Where you headed to?

MISS LYLE

New Orleans.

CONDUCTOR

You plannin' to get there on this railroad you going in the Smoking car.

Miss Lyle walks back to the Smoking car. Conductor notices a Black man about to sit down in the Ladies car next to a White woman. Conductor rushes forward.

CONDUCTOR

Boy! What you think you doin'?

BLACK MAN

The lady dropped something.

CONDUCTOR

He try to talk to you?

WHITE WOMAN

No.

Porter enters with silver tray, serving the White women lemonade.

CONDUCTOR

Get back there! (*Notices Ida who holds up her ticket as she reads from Frederick Douglas' autobiography.*) I can't accept this ticket. You'll have to move to the Smoking car.

IDA B. WELLS

I don't smoke.

CONDUCTOR

You tryin' to make my day difficult?

IDA B. WELLS

I'm trying to read this book.

CONDUCTOR

Go read it in the Smoking car.

IDA B. WELLS

I purchased a first class ticket which enables me to read it in the Ladies car.

CONDUCTOR

Not today, you ain't gone be reading no book in no Ladies car.

IDA B. WELLS

I guess I am.

CONDUCTOR

I'll be back.

Conductor moves to the Smoking car and punches tickets as the Black women continue to hold their hankies and cough.

WHITE WOMAN 1

Bad enough we got to educate them, now we suppose to sit next to them.

WHITE WOMAN 2

Conductor! Are you planning to serve lunch on this train?

CONDUCTOR

Yes Ma'am. Soon as we get goin'.

WHITE WOMAN 2

You are going to do something about "that situation" (*Pointing to Ida*) before you serve us?

CONDUCTOR

I'm working on it.

WHITE WOMAN 1

Working on it? (*She smiles.*)

WHITE WOMAN 2

This is Chancellor Dudley's wife who is addressing you, Conductor. If the Chancellor finds out you served his wife lunch sitting next to a Colored woman, well, if you plan to keep your job, you just don't want that to happen.

White women simultaneously open their fans and fluff themselves. Conductor forcefully approaches Ida.

CONDUCTOR

Move on back to the Smoking car, now!

IDA B. WELLS

There is plenty of room here.

CONDUCTOR

Get back there or get off the train!

Ida thrusts her legs onto the seat in front of her and braces herself.

WOMAN 1

She is jamming her legs in my seat!

WOMAN 2

This is outrageous, Conductor!

CONDUCTOR

(Grabbing Ida's arm) Let's go!

Ida bites the Conductor's hand.

WHITE WOMAN 2

She bit him!

WHITE WOMAN 1

You animal!

CONDUCTOR

(Shaking) You goin' to that Smoking car if I have to drag you by your hair!

IDA B. WELLS

Touch me again and I'll defend myself again!

CONDUCTOR

Start defending yourself cause you going. *(Conductor grabs Ida, who refuses to leave her seat.)* Porter get over here!

Conductor and Porter pull Ida out of her seat and thrust her onto the floor. Confusion amongst passengers in both cars, followed by complete silence and stillness as Ida slowly rises, brushes off her clothing, and speaks directly to the audience.

IDA B. WELLS

I purchased a first class ticket so that I could ride in the Ladies car. And I ask you, what makes any woman sitting there more of a lady than me? Is it the color of her skin or the price of her dress? I do not smoke. I do not drink alcohol. I am a schoolteacher, traveling alone. I say justice has not been served.

CONDUCTOR

Woodstock, Playton County. Connecting trains to New Orleans and Nashville.

Passengers exit disassembling railroad cars.

ELDERLY IDA

I decided to sue the Chesapeake and Ohio railroad.

PREACHER

Miss Ida! Where you off to?

IDA B. WELLS

I'm looking for Attorney Cassell, Preacher.

PREACHER

I heard you had some trouble, sorry to hear it.

IDA B. WELLS

I plan to do something about it.

PREACHER

For yourself or your people? Miss Ida, *The Free Speech* is the only Black newspaper in Memphis. You plan to sue the railroad, people need to know about it.

IDA B. WELLS

You going to put it in *The Free Speech*, Preacher?

PREACHER

That's right, and who better to write the story than Miss Ida B. Wells.

IDA B. WELLS

You want me to write for the newspaper?

PREACHER

That what God is telling me.

IDA B. WELLS

Who is going to listen to a school teacher?

PREACHER

Call yourself something different.

IDA B. WELLS

Iola?

PREACHER

Iola it is. I want the full story of what they did to you on that train. Write it. Sign it Iola. It's going into *The Free Speech*.

IDA B. WELLS

You got yourself a newspaper woman, Preacher!

Journalists rush in as women enter reading newspapers.

JOURNALIST

Extra! Extra! Read All About It!

JOURNALIST

Iola got the news! *Free Speech* coming out with it!

IDA B. WELLS

To the Negroes of Memphis, Tennessee! I must protest the conditions in the Colored schools!

WOMEN READERS

Our children have no books! Our children are made to sit on dirt floors! The classrooms are filled with rats and roaches!

JOURNALISTS

Miss Wells!

IDA B. WELLS

Gentlemen?

JOURNALIST

Are you the one signing your name, Iola?

IDA B. WELLS

I guess I am.

JOURNALIST

Would you like to comment on your recent editorial in *The Free Speech*?

IDA B. WELLS

I think my comments were quite clear.

JOURNALIST

Who do you hold responsible for the conditions in the Colored schools?

HEADMISTRESS

Miss Wells!

IDA B. WELLS

The Memphis School Board is responsible for both the White and the Colored schools.

JOURNALIST

What about this lawsuit?

CROWD

Lawsuit?

WOMEN

(Rhyme/Rap A modern beat.)
She had a first class ticket for the Ladies car.
He told her to move her butt to the Smoking car.
She don't care for the smell of a nasty cigar,
Wants to sit up front where the White ladies are!
Grabbed her ticket and tore it up
Bit his hand cause she had enough
Threw her from the seat and beat her down
Uncle Tom grinnin' she layin' on the ground.
White ladies cheer with a smile on their face
Ida thrown from the train in total disgrace.
She gonna fight this thing all the way
See what ole Judge Pierce has to say!
Ida B.!
Ida B.!

Crowd becomes the Courtroom.

CLERK

All rise. Judge James O. Pierce residing.

JUDGE PIERCE

In the matter of Chesapeake & Ohio & Southwestern Railroad Company versus Wells. Are all the parties present?

CONDUCTOR/IDA B. WELLS

Yes, your Honor.

JUDGE PIERCE

Then let's proceed. Who is here representing the railroad?

CONDUCTOR
I'm the one she bit, Judge.

JUDGE PIERCE
You bit him?

IDA B. WELLS
He was trying to take my seat.

JUDGE PIERCE
What does it cost to sit in the Ladies car, Conductor?

CONDUCTOR
Depend on where you going.

JUDGE PIERCE
Where was you going?

IDA B. WELLS
To Woodstock.

JUDGE PIERCE
How much does it cost to sit in the Ladies car from Memphis to Woodstock, Conductor?

CONDUCTOR
Cost you two dollars and a quarter.

JUDGE PIERCE
You pay two dollars and a quarter for your ticket?

IDA B. WELLS
Yes, your Honor.

JUDGE PIERCE
How much does it cost to sit in the Smoking car from Memphis to Woodstock, Conductor?

CONDUCTOR
(Whispering) Cost you a nickel and a dime.

JUDGE PIERCE
Speak up!

CONDUCTOR
Dime and a nickel.

JUDGE PIERCE
Fifteen cents?

CONDUCTOR
That's right.

JUDGE PIERCE
That's quite a difference, Conductor.

CONDUCTOR

Everybody can't afford a first class ticket.

JUDGE PIERCE

But Miss Wells purchased a first class ticket for the Ladies car.

CONDUCTOR

She was just there tryin' to stir up trouble!

JUDGE PIERCE

Order in the Court! Disrupt my court again and I will hold you in contempt. Now Miss Wells, why did you spend two dollars and twenty-five cents for a ticket, if you knew the Conductor was not going to let you use that ticket?

IDA B. WELLS

But I didn't know that, your Honor.

JUDGE PIERCE

What are you doing? Playing musical chairs on your railroad?

CONDUCTOR

Sometimes we let them sit in the Ladies car, sometimes we don't. Besides, I had to serve lunch to Chancellor Dudley's wife that day!

JUDGE PIERCE

How much did Chancellor Dudley's wife pay for her ticket?

CONDUCTOR

Two dollars and twenty-five cents.

JUDGE PIERCE

I'VE HEARD ABOUT ENOUGH OF THIS! Court rules in favor of Miss Ida B. Wells. Chesapeake and Ohio failed to provide Miss Wells with First Class accommodations after she had purchased a First Class ticket. Miss Wells is awarded damages of Five hundred dollars. Case dismissed.

Spectators in courtroom rise jubilantly as Journalists rush forward.

JOURNALIST

Get this on the press!

JOURNALIST

25TH OF DECEMBER, 1884.

JOURNALIST

The Memphis Daily Appeal. "A DARKY DAMSEL OBTAINS A VERDICT FOR DAMAGES AGAINST THE CHESAPEAKE & OHIO RAILROAD…"

JOURNALIST

What it cost to put a Colored Schoolteacher in a Smoking car…

JOURNALISTS

Verdict for five hundred dollars."

ELDERLY IDA

And I can still see those headlines, to this day.

PAGEANT THREE
The Memphis Lynchings

Ida enters reading papers, immediately sitting at newspaper desk typing furiously to make a deadline, as Elderly Ida opens her manuscript, dips her pen in the inkwell and begins to record a new chapter in her life.

ELDERLY IDA

The railroad case created quite a stir. I passed that city teacher's examination and worked in the Memphis Public schools. And every night I would burn the midnight oil. March 4, 1892.

JOURNALIST

Why did you take such a militant stand on education?

ELDERLY IDA

What was militant about wanting children to read?

Mrs. Washington and Mrs. Jefferson enter the newspaper office, journalists cover the story.

MRS. WASHINGTON

Miss Ida! Think you might put an article in *The Free Speech* about the church supper Sunday after next?

MRS. JEFFERSON

It's going to be a charity drive. We are gonna use all the money to buy new books for the children.

IDA B. WELLS

To the Negroes of Memphis! (*Journalists begin to write*) Beale Street Baptist Church is having a supper, Sunday after next, to raise money for schoolbooks. However, the School Board of Memphis is not going to allow those books into schools they control.

JOURNALIST

The fact is you don't keep to women's business.

ELDERLY IDA

To keep the waters troubled was to be awake while others slept.

JOURNALIST

What are you saying, Ida B. Wells?

IDA B. WELLS

What I am saying is this segregated South is going to make us second class citizens if we don't fight injustice.

MRS. WASHINGTON

Now hold on, Miss Ida! You gonna get yourself fired you don't learn to work with the system.

Mrs. Washington and Mrs. Jefferson exit.

ELDERLY IDA

The future of our race was my sole concern. But the road I chose was not without its lonely sorrow.

Journalists exit as Headmistress enters.

HEADMISTRESS
Miss Wells!

IDA B. WELLS
(*Filing papers she turns to Headmistress*) Ma'am?

HEADMISTRESS
When you came here 9 years ago, I gave you a job in the country schools.

IDA B. WELLS
Which I have performed to the best of my ability.

HEADMISTRESS
When you passed the city teachers examination, I gave you a job in the city schools.

IDA B. WELLS
Which I have performed to the best of my ability.

HEADMISTRESS
You have been earning sixty dollars a month as a Memphis schoolteacher!

IDA B. WELLS
Which I have earned.

HEADMISTRESS
Perhaps you can earn that from your newspaper writing!

IDA B. WELLS
What are you saying?

HEADMISTRESS
It is not what I am saying, Miss Wells. It is what you are writing!

IDA B. WELLS
The conditions in the colored schools are deplorable.

HEADMISTRESS
Most colored children have worst conditions in their own homes.

IDA B. WELLS
Can I quote you on that, Headmistress?

HEADMISTRESS
You are fired. (*Leaving in an agitated state.*)
You can clear out your desk at Clay County School.

ELDERLY IDA
I came into my own as a newspaper woman and became the Editor of *The Free Speech*.

Thomas Moss enters carrying the mail.

TOM MOSS
Mails here, Miss Ida !

IDA B. WELLS

Thank you, Tommie.

TOM MOSS

(*Hands her a stack of letters.*) Look who wants to carry the articles of Miss Ida B. Wells. *Chicago Defender. Detroit Plaindealer. Topeka Times Observer. New York Review!* They all want to hear what you got to say.

IDA B. WELLS

Appreciate that, Tommie.

TOM MOSS

Better open this one first! Special delivery from T. Thomas Fortune up in New York City.

IDA B. WELLS

T. Thomas Fortune! (*She rips open the large envelope*) The Editor of *The New York Age*! This is the biggest Black newspaper in New York City. He was born a slave in Florida, Tommie, now he is one of the most respected newspaper men in the country.

TOM MOSS

So what the letter say?

IDA B. WELLS

He wants me to write for his newspaper!

TOM MOSS

You can't leave Memphis!

IDA B. WELLS

He says the people up North need to know what's going on down here. T. Thomas Fortune wants to carry our news.

TOM MOSS

Bet he heard about that lynching over in Mississippi.

ELDERLY IDA

Issac Lupton. A colored boy of seventeen. Masked men broke into the city jail and strung him up.

TOM MOSS

Klan was behind that lynching, Miss Ida.

IDA B. WELLS

That's what I'm going to find out. Put it in T. Thomas Fortune's paper.

TOM MOSS

You going down to Greenville?

IDA B. WELLS

Gonna take the 5 o'clock.

TOM MOSS

No wonder you ain't got time for no man to catch up with you! (*Tommie's wife, Betty, walks in carrying her baby*) There's too much sweetness in this newspaper room for ten in the morning!

BETTY MOSS

I just came by to invite Ida for dinner.

TOM MOSS

What are we having?

BETTY MOSS

You know I cooks pot roast on Tuesday, Tommie.

TOM MOSS

You gonna make the dutch oven potatoes? Apple pie?

BETTY MOSS

Just rolled the crust out.

TOM MOSS

Wish you could come for Betty's pot roast and pie, Ida.

IDA B. WELLS

Next week when I come back.

BETTY MOSS

Where you going, Ida?

TOM MOSS

She going down to Mississippi! Then she headin' up to New York City!

BETTY MOSS

You always runnin' off somewhere, Ida.

TOM MOSS

Better get this mail delivered so I can get on down to the store.

BETTY MOSS

Tommie! You be careful.

TOM MOSS

Now don't start on that again, Betty. See you queens of Memphis later! *(Leaving from the front door)*

BETTY MOSS

Something goin' on down at that store, Ida. Tommie tryin' to keep it from me.

Calvin McDowell quickly walks in the back door.

CALVIN MCDOWELL

Morning Miss Ida, Miss Betty.

BETTY MOSS

Why isn't the store open, Calvin?

CALVIN MCDOWELL

Oh I'm about to open it. You seen Tommie?

BETTY MOSS

Is there trouble at the store, Calvin?

CALVIN MCDOWELL

Just wondered if Tommie'd been by yet.

IDA B. WELLS

You just missed him.

Calvin runs out the back door distracted as Willa Mae and Dora enter the front door.

WILLA MAE

Ida wait 'til you hear!

IDA B. WELLS

Girls it gone have to wait! I have to get this paper in order and be on a train by 5 o'clock. News can't wait.

WILLA MAE

That's why we here. Dora got some big news for you. Wait 'til you hear Betty.

BETTY MOSS

Is it about Calvin McDowell?

IDA B. WELLS

Miss Dora Johnson. Do you have some news for the Ladies page?

DORA

I guess I do, Miss Ida.

WILLA MAE

Show them the ring!

DORA

It's a real diamond.

WILLA MAE

Not many girls can say that.

IDA B. WELLS

It's fine, Dora.

BETTY MOSS

Finest one I ever saw.

WILLA MAE

Now wait! That is because you haven't seen mine!

BETTY/IDA

Henry?

WILLA MAE

Henry! We both got diamonds.

ELDERLY IDA

Dora and Willa Mae, engaged on the same day, now that was a story.

WILLA MAE

We gonna have a double wedding. You and Betty gots to be the Maids of Honor, Ida.

DORA

The two most eligible men in Memphis have been taken.

WILLA MAE

Make sure you put that in the paper!

DORA

Betty, what you think about selling some of your pies at the store?

BETTY MOSS

I don't know about that.

DORA

We need to help our men, make that store go.

WILLA MAE

Sure does make me feel good, knowing our people can put their money in Black hands.

IDA B. WELLS

The first colored grocery store in Memphis! Sure makes me proud! (*Noticing Betty falling away from the group*) What is it, Betty?

BETTY MOSS

Dream I had the other night. You was all in it. All three of you.

DORA

You musta been dreamin' about the wedding.

BETTY MOSS

It wasn't no good dream!

IDA B. WELLS

What you saying, Betty?

BETTY MOSS

We was all in that dream, but we wasn't wearin' white. Gots a bad feelin' about that store, can't shake it.

DORA

We all behind that grocery store.

BETTY MOSS

I'm a tellin' you, there gonna be trouble down there, the Lord tellin' me that, in my dreams!

Ida, Dora, Willa Mae and Betty walk into Betty's dream.

GRAND DRAGON

Bring them coons over here.

Hooded Klan push Tom Moss, Calvin McDowell, and Henry Stewart onto the ground.

KLAN
Bow your heads before the South, boys!

GRAND DRAGON
This is Judgement day!

TOM MOSS
We ain't done nothing.

GRAND DRAGON
Shut up!

TOM MOSS
We innocent men.

GRAND DRAGON
Men? Who you callin' men?

TOMMIE MOSS
I am a man that don't have to cover his face!

KLAN
You standing in front of the Grand Dragon, boy!

TOM MOSS
Three mens is standin' in front of you, cracker!

BETTY MOSS
Tommie! Don't talk back to that trash, they'll kill ya.

GRAND DRAGON
You got bucks up and down the Delta, what you care?

ELDERLY IDA
(*Walking into the dream*) You hurt those men, I swear to God, the whole country will hear about it.

GRAND DRAGON
You need to shut your mouth, nigger! Move 'em out!

Klan move Tom, Henry, and Calvin out.

DORA
Where you taking Calvin?

WILLA MAE
Where you taking Henry?

BETTY MOSS
Where you taking my husband?

GRAND DRAGON
Out ta Coon's creek to break his neck!

BETTY MOSS
Tommie!

Dream dissipates as Reverend Nightingale walks into the newspaper office.

REVEREND

Ladies.

LADIES

Reverend.

REVEREND

Reverend Jackson over in Greenville says that young man they lynched was deaf.

BETTY MOSS

I'm tellin' ya our men ain't safe down here.

IDA B. WELLS

What was the charge?

REVEREND

Said he stole a White woman's purse.

IDA B. WELLS

We are not gonna stand for this. I'm going over to get the facts, when I get to New York City, I am gonna put them in every newspaper in the country.

REVEREND

Here is your ticket.

IDA B. WELLS

Bless ya, Reverend. Betty thinks there is trouble down at the store.

BETTY MOSS

Trouble gone be at that store, Ida.

DORA

You go on.

WILLA MAE

We all be here when you get back.

IDA B. WELLS

Alright then. I'll see you all in a few weeks.

Ida dashes out to make the train.

ELDERLY IDA

I left *The Free Speech* and boarded a train for New York City on the day Memphis was about to write her history from the lynching tree.

HENRY STEWART

(*Running in*) Reverend! We need you down at the store.

REVEREND

I'm on my way.

WILLA MAE

What's goin' on, Henry?

HENRY STEWART

It ain't nothin', Willa Mae. Just best if folks see the Reverend down there.

WILLA MAE

Reverend, is you gonna tell us what's going on down there?

REVEREND

Seems to be some White trash down at the curb tryin' to stir up trouble.

The Newspaper Office swiftly becomes The People's Grocery Store. Tom Moss, Calvin McDowell, and Henry Stewart are busily waiting on customers who immediately fill the store.

MRS. WASHINGTON

Need six yards of your best wool, Tommie.

TOM MOSS

Got six yards to sell you, Mrs. Washington.

MRS. JEFFERSON

What kind of flour you got there, Calvin?

CALVIN MCDOWELL

White, rye and wheat. You makin' a cake, Mrs. Jefferson?

MRS. JEFFERSON

I guess I am.

Two White women, Miss Lily and her sister, Catherine, walk in.

MISS LILY

Tommie, you got the Sears Catalogue?

TOM MOSS

Right here, Miss Lily.

MISS LILY

Can you special order for me?

TOM MOSS

Just pick out what you want. We'll send out the order today.

Miss Lily and her sister peruse the catalogue.

Klan appear outside of the store.

GRAND DRAGON

I'm callin' you out tonight, 'cause Memphis is stinkin'!

KLAN

Stinkin'!

GRAND DRAGON

White man taken as much as he is gonna take. We got colored schools, a colored newspaper, and right in there, we got two White women in a colored grocery store!

KLAN

We need to burn it down!

GRAND DRAGON

That's why I brought you boys out here! We ain't gone have no Colored grocery store in Memphis. That's just the bottom line.

KLAN

What's the plan, Boss?

ELDERLY IDA

(*Watching from the side*) Took the Grand Dragon of Memphis less than a week to bring false charges against the Peoples' Grocery Store.

REVEREND

(*Rapidly entering grocery store.*) You got trouble out here, Tommie.

TOM MOSS

What's wrong, Reverend?

REVEREND

White man out here sayin' that one of you boys beat up his son.

TOM/CALVIN/HENRY

That's a lie!

REVEREND

He's bringing the Sheriff.

TOM MOSS

Sheriff?

REVEREND

Someone's gonna get locked up.

TOM MOSS

Excuse me, ladies, we gonna have to close up early today.

MRS. WASHINGTON

We stayin' right here, Tommie.

TOM MOSS

Calvin, cover the back. Henry, get that door.

REVEREND

We're all here with ya, Tommie.

TOM MOSS

Alright. Let 'em come.

An African American male with his face painted clown white, smoking a cigar, donned in Western style lawman attire calls out:

SHERIFF

Thomas Moss, Calvin McDowell, Henry Stewart.

TOM MOSS

We're in here.

SHERIFF

I got warrants for your arrest.

TOM MOSS

For what?

SHERIFF

Disturbing the peace down here at the curb.

TOM MOSS

We tryin' to run a business down here for our people.

HENRY STEWART

That's all we tryin' to do.

CALVIN MCDOWELL

It's your people tryin' to stir up trouble, Sheriff.

SHERIFF

Now you watch your mouth, boy. I'm here to protect you.

TOM MOSS

Protect us? Get them hooded Klan off the streets, you want to protect us.

SHERIFF

This a free country. Klan represent the White Knights of America in Memphis.

TOM MOSS

And we represent The People's Grocery Store in Memphis.

SHERIFF

Yeah, well, the People's Grocery Store is closed until further notice.

TOM MOSS

What you say?

SHERIFF

Thomas Moss, Calvin McDowell, Henry Stewart you are under arrest for aggravated assault, disturbing the peace, and operating an illicit business within Memphis city limits.

TOM MOSS

Illicit business?

SHERIFF

We have evidence that this grocery store is a cover for a den of iniquity.

CALVIN MCDOWELL

Sheriff, you know all three of us. We are deacons in our church.

TOM MOSS

This is about three Black men owning their own business, isn't it, Sheriff?

SHERIFF

I only know what the warrant says, Tommie.

TOM MOSS

And if we refuse to go?

SHERIFF

Resisting arrest? You do that, you prove your guilt.

TOM MOSS

What do you men want to do?

CALVIN MCDOWELL

What I want to do is go home.

HENRY STEWART

Every charge you have brought against us is a lie, Sheriff. But, we'll go to your jail, as law-abiding citizens of Memphis.

SHERIFF

Judge said he'd hear your case in less than a week.

TOM MOSS

Who gonna protect us in your jail, Sheriff?

SHERIFF

Nobody comin' near my jail. Promise you that as Sheriff of Memphis.

REVEREND

That gonna be enough to protect 'em?

SHERIFF

Just gave ya my word. (*Takes out handcuffs.*) Now, get over here.

Women begin a mournful humming as Sheriff handcuffs all three men. Betty, Dora, and Willa Mae run in.

BETTY MOSS

Where you takin' my husband?

DORA

Where you takin', Calvin?

WILLA MAE

Where you takin', Henry?

MRS. JEFFERSON

He takin' them to jail, that where he taking them!

Betty's legs go weak, she is supported by Willa Mae and Dora, both visibly shaking. Women stand in front of Sheriff, still humming.

SHERIFF

You makin' it worse than it is!

WOMEN

They innocent men!

SHERIFF

We gone let the court decide that! MOVE! (*Sheriff shoves the men out.*)

The soulful humming of the women bursts into a call and response song. Women slowly move all grocery items offstage, the table becomes the Sheriff's office. A small one room cell is rolled onstage, the three handcuffed men are placed in the cell by the Sheriff.

WOMAN

Calvin, Henry, Tommie.

WOMEN

Calvin, Henry, Tommie.

WOMAN

Moon shine bright over Memphis jail.

WOMAN

Don't let no lynchers come in there.

WOMAN

Calvin, Henry, Tommie.

WOMEN

Don't take them to that lynching tree!

The playing area darkens in a moment of stillness. The silhouettes of Tommie, Calvin, and Henry are discerned inside the Memphis jail. Sheriff is sitting with boots sprawled on his desk smoking a cigar. Reverend stands praying near the men clasping his bible.

ELDERLY IDA

Three nights passed in that Memphis jail. It was around three in the morning on March 9, 1892.

SHERIFF

Go on home, Reverend.

REVEREND

All the same, Sheriff, I'm staying right here.

SHERIFF

What you say? Get on outa here before I lock you up.

TOM MOSS

Reverend, do what he say.

CALVIN MCDOWELL

Judge gone hear our case in the morning.

HENRY STEWART

We all right, Reverend.

REVEREND

Let us pray.

SHERIFF

You been prayin' with them for three nights. Now, if the good Lord Jesus ain't heard you yet, He ain't listenin'!

REVEREND

Oh He listening. And watching too. Believe that, Sheriff. Lord is looking at all this business.

SHERIFF

You ain't got no more business here!

REVEREND

Be back first thing in the morning. *(Reverend leaves.)*

MEN

All right, Reverend.

SHERIFF

Now, maybe I can get some sleep. You boys do the same.

TOM MOSS

We ain't gonna be doing no sleepin' here!

SHERIFF

Boy, thirty years ago you would be dead for talkin' like that!

TOM MOSS

What that suppose to mean?

CALVIN MCDOWELL

We ain't no slaves on your plantation.

SHERIFF

Yeah, but you three coons locked up in my jail.

Sheriff looks at his watch and leaves. Hooded Klan strut in.

CALVIN MCDOWELL

Lord, Tommie! Look over there!

HENRY STEWART

Where the Sheriff go?

TOM MOSS

Sheriff! Get back in here!

KLAN MEMBER

Look at the coons in the cage.

TOM MOSS
We under the protection of Memphis law!

KLAN MEMBER
You lookin' at Memphis law!

TOM MOSS
We scheduled for court in the morning.

Grand Dragon in hooded red robe appears.

GRAND DRAGON
We holding court, tonight!

MEN
SHERIFF!

KLAN MEMBER
Grand Dragon Judge, presiding.

GRAND DRAGON
Let's get down to it. You three are guilty as hell.

TOM MOSS
Guilty of what?

GRAND DRAGON
Of what? Of that grocery store, that's what!

TOM MOSS
It's a legal business.

CALVIN MCDOWELL
We are honest men.

GRAND DRAGON
Only men in Memphis are White! You think cause you wear White man's clothes, that make you a man? Cause you work at the Post Office? Let me tell you something, my Daddy owned the coons that bred ya! They wasn't no men, and you ain't no men, and we sure as hell ain't gonna have no nigger grocery store in Memphis.

TOM MOSS
The men that make up the city of Memphis are Black and White. Don't matter if you kill us, you can't change that fact.

GRAND DRAGON
Lynch the bastards.

TOM MOSS
Sheriff!

HENRY STEWART
This ain't no trial!

GRAND DRAGON

Where the Sheriff with them keys?

Sheriff walks in and unlocks the jail. Klan grab the three handcuffed men and shove them onto their knees. Klan stand towering over the men.

TOM MOSS

You in on this, Sheriff?

GRAND DRAGON

That switch engine ready?

SHERIFF

3:20. Conductor got the train ready.

TOM MOSS

What's goin' on here?

SHERIFF

Where you gone dump the bodies?

TOM MOSS

Sheriff! Look at me!

GRAND DRAGON

We gone dump them about a mile north of the city limits.

SHERIFF

I'll wait 'til around noon to send my boys out there to find 'em.

TOM MOSS

We ain't guilty!

CALVIN MCDOWELL

Sheriff! You suppose to protect us! You gave the Reverend your word.

SHERIFF

I did. But that was before I had to smell ya for three nights. Gone take me a week to get your stink outa my jail.

HENRY STEWART

You ain't no Sheriff!

Sheriff pulls out his gun and shoots Henry in the head. Henry slumps over.

CALVIN MCDOWELL

Henry! You killed him!

TOM MOSS

Stop this! Grocery store closed! I got a wife and child. I'm beggin' ya, stop!

GRAND DRAGON

(Pointing gun at Tom) Those your last words?

TOM MOSS

Tell my people to go West. There is no justice in Memphis.

Grand Dragon shoots Tom. Tom slumps over. Calvin breaks free of his handcuffs and grabs the gun, which goes off in his hand. The Klan shoots him in the face. Calvin slumps over.

GRAND DRAGON

Get 'em outa here!

The sound of a passing train intermingles with the mournful humming of women entering. A sorrowful Wade in the Water rendition is sung. The bodies are removed.

ELDERLY IDA

The bodies were found at twelve noon on March 10, 1892.

Sheriff walks in and sits at his desk. The Reverend and women cross over to Sheriff.

SHERIFF

I don't know what happened.

REVEREND

Where were you?

SHERIFF

Lying on my cot, in the back.

MRS. JEFFERSON

You didn't see nothin'?

SHERIFF

Nothin'.

REVEREND

Were they wearing hoods?

SHERIFF

It was dark! Couldn't see a thing!

MRS. JEFFERSON

Somebody sure saw them keys!

REVEREND

Klan did this. You know it, and I know it.

SHERIFF

I don't know nothin'!

MRS. JEFFERSON

You know three mens was murdered!

ELDERLY IDA

Nobody knew nothing.

Criminal Judge enters with a striking resemblance in gait and stature to the Grand Dragon.

CRIMINAL JUDGE

Sheriff! I am issuing an order! Take a hundred men out to the curb at once, and shoot on sight any Negro who appears to be making trouble. *(Rushes out.)*

SHERIFF

Yes sir!

Sheriff jumps up and begins to shoot at the crowd who disperse throughout the playing area.

ELDERLY IDA

Sheriff took a mob out to the curb. "They took possession of the People's Grocery Store, and destroyed what they could not eat or steal." The news reached me in Natchez, Mississippi and I headed back to Memphis. "*The Free Speech* felt that it must carry on."

IDA B. WELLS

(With suitcase in hand, rushing in) To the Negroes of Memphis! "The city of Memphis has demonstrated that neither character nor standing avails the Negro if he dares to protect himself against the White man or become his rival."

ELDERLY IDA

"There is therefore only one thing left that we can do; save our money and leave a town which will neither protect our lives and property, nor give us a fair trial in the courts, but takes us out and murders us in cold blood when accused by White persons."

PAGEANT FOUR
Crusade for Justice

REVEREND

I'm asking everyone of you to come with me. They about to open up Oklahoma! Cause I ain't gonna live in Memphis!

CROWD

We ain't gone live in Memphis!

DORA

I won't wear clothes bought from a White man's store.

WILLA MAE

I won't eat food bought from a White man's store.

BETTY MOSS

When my husband sold goods to our people, they took him out and shot him like a dog!

CROWD

Shot him down!

REVEREND

My church ain't got no more business in Memphis!

WHITE WOMAN
Jewelry half off! For the first time, Gimbal's is offering you colored women credit!

CROWD
We don't want your credit!

WHITE WOMAN
You can't bring that furniture back in here! You ladies bought it on the savings plan!

CROWD
We don't want your savings plan.

Crowd clears the playing area as Ida begins writing an editorial at typewriter as Criminal Judge enters Free Speech office.

CRIMINAL JUDGE
Ida B. Wells?

IDA B. WELLS
Miss Ida B. Wells.

CRIMINAL JUDGE
You need to write something in your paper.

IDA B. WELLS
That's just what I am doing.

CRIMINAL JUDGE
You need to write something to stop this exodus from Memphis.

IDA B. WELLS
It has been six weeks since the lynching, Judge.

CRIMINAL JUDGE
And Memphis Negroes are destroying the city's business.

IDA B. WELLS
How is that?

CRIMINAL JUDGE
They ain't buying! They ain't riding the city's streetcars! They leaving houses with mortgages and heading West.

IDA B. WELLS
You think I can stop that?

CRIMINAL JUDGE
Your people listen to you.

IDA B. WELLS
And I'm telling them to go West!

CRIMINAL JUDGE
What?

IDA B. WELLS

Did you know Tommie Moss, Judge?

CRIMINAL JUDGE

I did.

IDA B. WELLS

He was the finest man that ever walked the streets of Memphis.

CRIMINAL JUDGE

That's quite a weight your putting on his shoulders. But, since he's one of yours and dead...

IDA B. WELLS

He is dead because he was murdered with no more consideration than if he had been a dog.

CRIMINAL JUDGE

It's unfortunate. However, that grocery store had people stirred up.

IDA B. WELLS

Why would anyone object to colored men owning their own business?

CRIMINAL JUDGE

Do you know who was in that grocery store the day they were arrested?

IDA B. WELLS

Enlighten me.

CRIMINAL JUDGE

Two White women.

IDA B. WELLS

And?

CRIMINAL JUDGE

Two White women! They was buying food in there!

IDA B. WELLS

What you suppose to buy in a grocery store?

CRIMINAL JUDGE

You are missing the point! Anything could have happened to those women in there!

IDA B. WELLS

Tommie Moss, Calvin McDowell, and Henry Stewart were lynched because they sold groceries to White women? Please tell me that is not what you're trying to tell me!

CRIMINAL JUDGE

The Southern White man is not going to have his woman's honor compromised, Miss Wells.

ELDERLY IDA

The Criminal Court Judge was the Grand Dragon himself.

CRIMINAL JUDGE

Those lynchings were six weeks ago. Your people need to let it rest.

IDA B. WELLS

There have been seventeen lynchings reported to my office in the last six weeks.

CRIMINAL JUDGE

Your people have to learn to live by the law.

IDA B. WELLS

A man is innocent until tried by a jury. What laws are you talking about?

CRIMINAL JUDGE

I'm talking about the Southern White man. His way of life, that was destroyed by the war. Your people shouting so much about freedom, now that they got it, what they doing with it?

IDA B. WELLS

Tommie, Calvin, and Henry were doing just fine with theirs!

CRIMINAL JUDGE

They're dead! Nothing you can do can change that!

IDA B. WELLS

That's where you are wrong, Judge! I'm gonna keep their names alive in my paper! I am gonna let the whole country know they were innocent men, hard working men, Black men. They were lynched by cowards who could walk up and down the South and never fill their shoes. They alive, you understand me? They alive!

CRIMINAL JUDGE

What you plan to do? Turn this into a lynching paper?

IDA B. WELLS

This is *The Free Speech*, Judge. Where people are not afraid of the truth.

CRIMINAL JUDGE

I came here in good faith.

IDA B. WELLS

No! You came in here to tell me that the lives of Tommie, Calvin, and Henry didn't matter. Long as the White man controls business, schools, everything is gonna be fine in Memphis. But you do not control my newspaper!

CRIMINAL JUDGE

Why don't you go out and find the guilty ones?

IDA B. WELLS

Suppose I had the evidence?

CRIMINAL JUDGE

What evidence you got?

IDA B. WELLS

Does it matter? There won't be an indictment against a White man in this town for those murders.

CRIMINAL JUDGE

You watch what you put in that paper.

IDA B. WELLS

To the Negroes of Memphis!

Crowd rushes in.

IDA B. WELLS

21ST OF MAY, 1892. Eight Negroes lynched since last issue of *The Free Speech*. One at Little Rock, Arkansas last Saturday morning where the citizens broke into the jail and got their man. Three lynched near Anniston, Alabama. One lynched near New Orleans for looking at a White woman. Five lynched in Clarksville, Georgia for stealing corn husks. "Nobody in this section of the country believes the old threadbare lie that Negro men rape White women." That was the editorial as I wrote in on the 21st of May, 1892. As it went to press I boarded a train for New York City. (*She leaves.*)

SHERIFF

Ida B. Wells!

REVEREND

Miss Wells headed for New York City six days ago.

SHERIFF

Hand over the keys. Newspaper's closed.

REVEREND

You have a court order?

CRIMINAL JUDGE

(*Entering*) I am the court order! Clear it out!

ELDERLY IDA

The mob descended on the offices of *The Free Speech*.

Klan cross to Criminal Judge with Grand Dragon suit, he puts on his red robe as he gives orders.

CRIMINAL JUDGE

This press go over to Montgomery. Get the type to Watson. Bulk paper belong to Johnson. This office is returned to Davis. To the Negroes of Memphis! May 27th 1892. *The Free Speech* is closed. Any Negro attempting to publish this paper again will be shot.

Criminal Judge and Klan swiftly exit.

ELDERLY IDA

I was never to return to Memphis, but my crusade for justice had just begun.

JOURNALIST

Get this on the press!

JOURNALIST

June 4, 1892.

IDA B. WELLS

Five Negroes lynched in Greenville, South Carolina.

JOURNALIST

What was the charge?

ELDERLY IDA

Swimming in a water hole that was on private property.

JOURNALIST

July 24, 1893.

IDA B. WELLS

Three Black men riddled in bullets in Mobile, Alabama.

JOURNALIST

Was there a trial?

ELDERLY IDA

If there had been a trial there wouldn't have been a lynching.

JOURNALIST

Get this on the press!

JOURNALIST

Nashville, Tennessee.

IDA B. WELLS

"With Governor Buchanan and the police standing by, Ephan Grizzard was dragged through the streets in broad daylight, knives plunged unto him at every step, they strung him to the bridge and when he grabbed the rails, they cut his hands to pieces."

ELDERLY IDA

Between 1892 and 1902, lynching was common practice in the South. It was a hard truth and I was full of indignation against this injustice.

JOURNALIST

What was the real reason for lynching?

ELDERLY IDA

Go back to Reconstruction and examine the real facts of American history.

JOURNALIST

Resentment over the war?

ELDERLY IDA

That was part of it. Southerners began to realize that God had made men in all colors, and it was a frightening revelation. Resentment of Black advancement was the real cause of lynching. That is why they killed my brothers in Memphis!

JOURNALIST

Get this on the press!

JOURNALIST

1895. Ida B. Wells takes her cause to England!

JOURNALIST

Miss Ida B. Wells has crossed the Atlantic to let the British hear first hand the atrocities Black men in the southern United States are facing thirty years after the Civil War.

JOURNALIST
You went to England to speak out against lynching?

IDA B. WELLS
And Sweden.

JOURNALIST
Who funded your campaign?

ELDERLY IDA
Courageous women in Europe.

JOURNALIST
But didn't you say that White women were involved in lynching?

IDA B. WELLS
The Ku Klux Klan used their own women in the South as an excuse to lynch Black men.

JOURNALIST
How long were you involved in your crusade for justice?

ELDERLY IDA
(Closing her manuscript and leaving.) All my life.

JOURNALIST
March 25, 1931.

JOURNALIST
Ida B. Wells-Barnett died today in Chicago, Illinois. She was sixty-eight years old.

Crowd begins to hum, Wade in the Water.

JOURNALIST
The sidewalks are filled with people, both Black and White, who have come to pay their respect for the Princess of the Press.

As the crowd stroll, various people from Ida's life step forth.

JIM WELLS
Look out for your people.

ELIZABETH WELLS
I wanna hear nothing but the Word of God in my house on Sunday.

MISSIONARY
And the earth shone with His Glory.

GRANDMA PEGGY
Come over here, chile so we can let that dress down!

REVEREND
Cause it's a new day in Mississippi!

SISTAH JEFFERSON
I was stripped and beaten for tryin' to read the holy book.

CONDUCTOR

Sometimes we let the colored women sit up here, sometimes we don't.

ELDERLY IDA

Youth are entitled to the facts of race history.

EUGENIA

They gonna send me away, Ida?

HEADMISTRESS

These are excellent scores for a colored girl.

JOURNALIST

Crowds have been standing out here in the cold for six hours to pay their respects!

IDA B. WELLS

I do not smoke. I do not drink alcohol. I am a schoolteacher traveling alone.

SHERIFF

Thomas Moss, Calvin McDowell, Henry Stewart! You're under arrest.

IDA B. WELLS

You hurt those men, I swear the whole country will hear about it!

GRAND DRAGON

We ain't gonna have no colored grocery store in Memphis!

TOM MOSS

I am a man that don't have to cover his face!

BETTY MOSS

When my husband sold goods to my people, they took him out and shot him like a dog.

MISSIONARY

And the sound of His coming was like the sound of many waters…

CAST

(Singing) God's gonna trouble the waters…..

ELDERLY IDA

To keep the waters troubled.

Fade to black

End of Play

HISTORICAL SOURCES
Writings by Ida B. Wells-Barnett 1862-1931

Duster, Alfreda, *Crusade for Justice: The Autobiography of Ida B. Wells*, Chicago: University of Chicago Press, 1970.

Free Speech, "Eight Men Lynched" Editorial by Miss Ida B. Wells, May 21, 1892.

"Lynch Law in Georgia" pamphlet by Miss Ida B. Wells, (1899).

"Mob Rule in New Orleans. Robert Charles and His Fight to the Death. the story of His Life. Burning Human Being Alive. Other Lynching Statistics." pamphlet by Miss Ida B. Wells, Chicago (1900).

"Southern Horros. Lynch :aw in All Its Phases" pamphlet by Miss B. Wells, New York. (1892).

Wells, Ida B. *A Red Record. Tabuulated Statistics and Alleged Causes of Lynchings in The United States, 1892-1893-1894.* (1895).

MEAN MOLLY
An African Folktale of the Deep South
by Carolyn Nur Wistrand

CHARACTERS

Mean Molly/Nomikonto - A dead African haunted by the African spirit of Obonto.

Watah Mocassion - An African/Seminole trapper who hunts the rice swamps.

Miss Laura - An elderly Negro woman of the Deep South.

Chicken Leg - Miss Laura's son. An avid reader, he masks his intelligence.

Dr. Jeb Lucas - A con artist who served as a medical assistant in the Union Army during the Civil War, calls himself a doctor.

Main Man - First son of Chicken Leg.

Baby Brother - Second son of Chicken Leg

Massah George - Owner of Cypress Plantation

Obonto - Spirit of Ijebu warrior of Benin, West Africa

Preacher - Self-taught country man.

African Drummers

SETTING - *The rice swampland, South Carolina*   TIME - *1866*

ONE
Marked at the graveyard hole

Midnight. A water hole, near a graveyard, in the rice swampland of South Carolina. Sounds of African drums come up. The spirit of a dead African girl runs in to the call of the drums. She dances in a frenzied otherworldly plea to her Ancestors. Hurling her body into spirit filled contortions and jumping on a tree stump, she cries out:

MEAN MOLLY

Obanto!

Night sounds of swampland come up as the drums soften. Watah Mocasin appears with fishing pole and bucket. He sets down the bucket, takes out a can of worms, and talks to the fish.

WATAH MOCASIN

You fish hungry? Look here what Mocasin got for ya.

MEAN MOLLY

Obonto!

Watah Mocasin throws out the line as Mean Molly lunges at his back. Watah Mocasin slaps his back, like he is hitting a mosquito.

WATAH MOCASIN

Get off me.

MEAN MOLLY

(Clawing at the air in the direction of his back) Obonto!

WATAH MOCASIN

(Drops fishing pole and looks around) Some varmin out here I don't see? C'mon. Show yourself you got something to say.

MEAN MOLLY

Obonto!

WATAH MOCASIN

Animal, human, haunt, tell me what you want!

MEAN MOLLY

(Twirls around him crying out) E si ye!

WATAH MOCASIN

I heard ya that time! You a haunt!

WATAH MOCASIN

(Pacing) You ain't got to be scared a me. Shoot. Might be kin to me. Is you kin?

MEAN MOLLY

E si ye mo le.

WATAH MOCASIN

I don't know what you saying.

MEAN MOLLY

E si ye mo le!

WATAH MOCASIN

You a African spirit?

MEAN MOLLY

Not be I leave.

WATAH MOCASIN

Leave. That's right. You just go on and leave.

MEAN MOLLY

Obonto!

WATAH MOCASIN

You one of dem African slaves buried over there?

MEAN MOLLY

Nwon Ni Ki O Ru.

WATAH MOCASIN

Lord have mercy! You ain't Mean Molly is ya?

MEAN MOLLY

O ni ki o pe.

A sharp pain begins to penetrate Watah Mocasin's back.

WATAH MOCASIN

What wrong with my back? This my blood! You trying to kill me? I don't know what you is…but you go back! You hear what I'm sayin'? GO BACK TO DAT GRAVE!

Watah Mocasin grabs his fishing pole and bucket, running off as the drums call to the African spirit of the dead slave.

MEAN MOLLY

In the spring of 1866 of our Lord,
America just fight the great Civil War.
All the African buried here as slaves,
Sleep in sweet grass,
Free in their graves.
Mean Molly not free in no sharecropper dirt.
That why she haunt!
That way she hurt!
Obonto! (*Raises her hands and runs towards the sound of the drums*)

TWO
Legal Papers

The next morning. May, 1866. Nine African masks, brightly painted, stand surrounding slave shacks left over from Cypress plantation. Miss Laura's shack is discerned on one side of the playing area. An old rocking chair sits on her front porch, a pan of biscuits, bucket of water, and cup are next to the rocking chair. Large pots, sack of flour, bucket of grease, spices, and assorted cooking utensils are arranged on an old wooden table. Chicken Leg's shack is discerend on the other side of the playing area. Two wooden chairs, bucket, assorted tools, and crate of old rags, surround his shack.

Miss Laura sits in rocking chair snapping beans as Chicken Leg limps in with a burlap bag and hoe.

CHICKEN LEG

Lord! This leg 'bout to do me in, Mama.

MISS LAURA

Ain't even noon boy! You gots a full day of pickin' in front of you.

CHICKEN LEG

(Puts down his bag and hoe) Gone have to wait.

MISS LAURA

Get back out there 'fore the sun heat up!

CHICKEN LEG

(Scoops a cup of water from the bucket) I gots to see Dr. Lucas.

MISS LAURA

(Rising, throws beans in a large kettle) That man ain't no more a doctah than he is the president.

CHICKEN LEG

You been inside my pain to know? He a doctah from Cincinnatti, Ohio.
They gots a big school up there for doctahs, 'n he gots papers from that school!

MISS LAURA

How you know where his papers from?

CHICKEN LEG

(Grabbing a biscuit) Dr. Lucas told me where they from!

MISS LAURA

How you know what them papers say?

CHICKEN LEG

Dr. Lucas told me what they say!

MISS LAURA

(Scoops grease out of pail and slaps it into her beans) You can't even read, Chicken Leg.
(Shoving him out of the way) You make me tired just looking at you.

CHICKEN LEG

What you talking about I can't read? Signed the deed on my house! Guess I read them papers before I signed them. I can read my name. Write it too!

MISS LAURA

I ain't talkin' 'bout yoh name! Ah'm a talkin' 'bout all the words on the paper 'fore they gets to yoh name!

CHICKEN LEG

(*Grabbing another biscuit*) They didn't say much. Important thing was the place where I sign my name. That mean I own my house.

MISS LAURA

You don't know what on dat paper you sign.

CHICKEN LEG

What on de paper Abraham Lincoln sign?

MISS LAURA

You still carryin' dat ole newpaper 'round?

CHICKEN LEG

'Til the day I die. Plenty a these crackers don't know how to read!

MISS LAURA

Everybody know what on dat paper!

CHICKEN LEG

"That on the first day of January, in the year of our Lord, One Thousand Eight Hundred and Sixty-Three, All persons held as slaves within any state, shall be forever free." You know I read the words, read them in this paper. Fact is I read them to you, Mama.

MISS LAURA

I don't remember all that.

She quickly sweeps turning her back on Chicken Leg. He follows his mother, shoving the deed to his house in her face.

CHICKEN LEG

You remember this? Signed it last week at the Freedman's Bureau. This the deed to my house and 2 acres of this rice swampland.

MISS LAURA

That 's what Ah'm a talkin' about! How you know what dat paper say?

CHICKEN LEG

I can read it, Mama! Charles Foster Spencer having paid in full, thirty seven dollars, is hereby the rightful owner of 2 acres of land formerly known as Cypress Plantation. Deed of owner-ship signed on this day, 17th of May, 1866 of our Lord in Gullah County, South Carolina, United States of America. Let 'em come in here 'n try 'n take it from me.

MISS LAURA

You sure dat say you own 2 acres?

CHICKEN LEG

On Daddy's grave.

MISS LAURA

Don't be puttin' dat paper on yoh Daddy's grave.

CHICKEN LEG
DON'T BE SAYING I CANT READ THE PAPER I PUT MY NAME TO!

MISS LAURA
Take yoh paper and go work dem 2 acres.

CHICKEN LEG
Ah tole ya Ah'ma waitin' on Dr. Lucas.

MISS LAURA
All he gots is poison make ya too lazy ta work!

CHICKEN LEG
Ah ain't got time to hear all this!

MISS LAURA
You got time to eat up all my biscuits.

CHICKEN LEG
Put a chicken in the pot. Forget them biscuits.

MISS LAURA
Go on.

THREE
Carpetbag medicine man

Dr. Jeb Lucas strolls in, dressed in cheap traveling salesman attire, carrying a carpetbag filled with medicine. A small time con artist, his crude medical knowledge is the result of serving in the Union army as a medical assistant. He now disguises himself as a doctor in the rural South, passing off a homemade mixture of corn liquor and sweet juice as medicine. 1866 has been a good year for the doctor.

JEB LUCAS
How you feeling today, Miss Laura?

MISS LAURA
I don't want to be smelling no liquor at my supper!

CHICKEN LEG
Go on inside, Mama. Me and the doctah gots business.

Miss Laura saunters to the back of her shack, muttering to herself.

JEB LUCAS
Got some medicine for ya.

CHICKEN LEG
That's what I been waiting on. Come on over to my place.

They cross over to Chicken Leg's shack. Chicken Leg sits in one of the chairs, Jeb Lucas carefully puts his suitcase on the work table, then sits in the other chair.

CHICKEN LEG

This leg be going out on me, Dr. Jeb.

JEB LUCAS

Let's take a look at it.

CHICKEN LEG

(Rolling up his pant leg) Ah ain't put in two hours this morning before it took all my strength to stand.

Jeb enjoys his "doctoring", a sense of pride overcomes him as he feels and pokes Chicken Leg.

JEB LUCAS

So who working your crop?

CHICKEN LEG

My boys.

JEB LUCAS

That hurt?

CHICKEN LEG

Yes sir. Ohhh…right there. My boys big and strong. Put in 12 hours, 6 days a week.

Lucas finishes the examination, and lights his pipe.

JEB LUCAS

Lord gave you some good sons.

CHICKEN LEG

Ah knows that's right.

JEB LUCAS

Lord gave you one good leg.

CHICKEN LEG

Uh Hum.

JEB LUCAS

One good leg, worth 4 hours of fieldwork. Rest of your time, you let them boys make up. They good workers. Now..let's talk business.

Jeb takes a small black notebook and pen out of his coat pocket.

JEB LUCAS

(Ceremoniously) May 17 medical visit…2 bottle…2 dollars. May 21 medical visit…1 bottle…1 dollar. Today is May 24, 1866, you takin' one or two bottles?

CHICKEN LEG

That depend on how many you give me.

JEB LUCAS

How many you got the money for?

CHICKEN LEG

Got the money for two, but can't get to it right now.

JEB LUCAS

You got the money for one?

CHICKEN LEG

I get it to you Tuesday.

JEB LUCAS

I need my money today! Tuesday, I'll be in Rock Hill.

CHICKEN LEG

Can't cash in my crops 'til Tuesday.

JEB LUCAS

I been out here three times…you ain't paid me yet.

CHICKEN LEG

Appreciate that.

JEB LUCAS

Doctorin' a business…just like farmin'. You need to pay.

CHICKEN LEG

You get yoh money. Come back Tuesday.

JEB LUCAS

Your doctor bill due today.

CHICKEN LEG

You a smart man, Dr. Jeb.

JEB LUCAS

That's what they said at that school up in Cincinatti, Ohio. They said, "Jeb Lucas, You a smart man. Put Doctor in front of your name." Did I ever show you the papers they give me? *(Takes out his Union discharge papers.)*

CHICKEN LEG

Which word say Doctah?

JEB LUCAS

Well..let's see here…*(puts on his spectacles)* this word…no…here it is…this word right here… say Doctor. Doctor Jeb Lucas.

CHICKEN LEG

Yeah, you a doctah foh sure. Other one come around here don't know nothing.

JEB LUCAS

There been another Doctor around here?

CHICKEN LEG

Foh sure. Dr. Burt come 'round here once 'ta month. Never say nothin' bout money.

JEB LUCAS

He don't work for free do he?

CHICKEN LEG
What you think he tell me 'bout my leg?

JEB LUCAS
Your leg?

CHICKEN LEG
He say wrap it.

JEB LUCAS
Wrap it?

CHICKEN LEG
That all he say. Wrap it. "After work, wrap it." I tell him, Dr. Jeb Lucas don't say nothing about wrappin' my leg.

JEB LUCAS
You told him 'bout me?

CHICKEN LEG
Foh sure. He say he never hear a no Dr. Jeb Lucas.

JEB LUCAS
Well I ain't ever heard a no Dr. Burt!

CHICKEN LEG:
I tell him, "Ya never heard of him, cause he from Cincinatti, Ohio!"

JEB LUCAS:
That's right! Where folks pay their bill!

FOUR
Sewin' up the back

Watah Mocasin runs in hysterically.

CHICKEN LEG
Watah Mocasin! They bitin'?

WATAH MOCASIN
Something bit me!

CHICKEN LEG
What you talking?

WATAH MOCASIN
Dr. Burt around?

CHICKEN LEG
He over in Hemingway. Miss White about to pass.

WATAH MOCASIN

I gots to see him!

CHICKEN LEG

Sit down, boy. You looking at a real Doctah!

WATAH MOCASIN

You a doctah?

JEB LUCAS

What's wrong with you, boy?

WATAH MOCASIN

Back bleedin' all nite.

JEB LUCAS

Let's take a look.

Watah Mocasin takes off his shirt, exposing bloody marks all over his back.

CHICKEN LEG

Dang! What cat did that?

JEB LUCAS

Ya need to be sewed up.

WATAH MOCASIN

I wait on Dr. Burt.

Jeb goes over to his suitcase and retrieves a needle and thread.

JEB LUCAS

Ain't nothing to sewing you up, boy. Rode with Sherman in the War. Sewed up arms, legs, chests, feet with no toes. You got any money on you?

WATAH MOCASIN

Forty eight cents.

JEB LUCAS

Enough to stop blood.

Mocasin hands coins to Lucas. Lucas counts coins and hands Mocasin his flask.

WATAH MOCASIN

What this?

JEB LUCAS

Forty eight cents a medicine. I'll throw in the operation.

CHICKEN LEG

Go on! It knock out the pain.

Watah Mocasin drinks the medicine. Lucas threads the needle.

JEB LUCAS

Need a rag.

Chicken Leg grabs an old rag sitting on a pot.

CHICKEN LEG

This cooking rag?

JEB LUCAS

That'll do.*(Drips medicine on the rag.)* Alright, boy. Bend over. Clean this out.

CHICKEN LEG

(Staring at Mocasin's back) That just what Uncle Ivory look like.

WATAH MOCASIN

It look that bad?

CHICKEN LEG

Uh hum.

Jeb Lucas is now ready to stitch up Mocasin's back. He learned to sew up soldiers in the War and performs the procedure with skill.

JEB LUCAS

Grab that stick. Shove it in his mouth.

Chicken Leg grabs a stick and shoves it in Mocasin's mouth.

JEB LUCAS

Just bite when it stings, boy. Yeah, I never seen so many arms and legs shot up as when we took that march. Wasn't for Sherman, this would still be Confederate land.

CHICKEN LEG

Abraham Lincoln the president down here…even when Jefferson Davis president. He de man save the Union.

JEB LUCAS

That 'n a yankee dollar couldn't buy you a cupa coffee around here 'til Sherman took that ride to Atlanta. Yeah, he sure tore up the South…Watah Mocasin, you holding up good.

CHICKEN LEG

He can take it. Massah George used ta beat him bad.

JEB LUCAS

Who?

CHICKEN LEG

Massah used to own everything 'round here. Land, cotton, rice, human..only thing free was de alligator down in de swamp. He dead.

WATAH MOCASIN

(Takes stick out of his mouth) I killed him.

CHICKEN LEG

You a lie! I killed Massah George.

WATAH MOCASIN

You a lie!

JEB LUCAS
Hold Still!

CHICKEN LEG
Mean Molly the one kill Massah George. Everybody know it.

JEB LUCAS
That should take care of you.

CHICKEN LEG
That sure look like the mark come on Uncle Ivory.

WATAH MOCASIN
Why you keep sayin' that?

CHICKEN LEG
Where you get it?

WATAH MOCASIN
Don't know.

CHICKEN LEG
You fishin' down by the graveyard?

WATAH MOCASIN
No.

CHICKEN LEG
You knows better.

WATAH MOCASIN
What you talking about?

CHICKEN LEG
Mean Molly what I'm talking about!

FIVE
De African out de graveyard

Miss Laura appears on her porch.

MISS LAURA
What's goin' on out here?

CHICKEN LEG
He been down to the water hole, Mama!

MISS LAURA
You been down there, boy?

WATAH MOCASIN
No Ma'am.

CHICKEN LEG
> You a Lie! Lift up that shirt, boy!

WATAH MOCASIN
> Uh uh. Tell' 'em ah'ma sick, Doctah!

MISS LAURA
> He don't need to tell me nothin'! Ah'ma talkin' to you!

WATAH MOCASIN
> Dey ain't bitin at de lake, Miss Laura.

MISS LAURA
> So you took it in yoh mind to go over to de graveyard hole?

CHICKEN LEG
> Speak up, boy! She talkin' to ya!

WATAH MOCASIN
> Ah can't remember.

MISS LAURA
> You want leeches start comin' out yoh back?

JEB LUCAS
> Leeches? I just sewed the boy up.

MISS LAURA
> You touch his blood?

JEB LUCAS
> Blood part a doctorin'.

MISS LAURA
> Blood from de graveyard hole dangerous!

CHICKEN LEG
> You gone die, Mocasin!

WATAH MOCASIN
> Miss Laura! Ya gots ta help me!

JEB LUCAS
> Ain't nothin' wrong with you, boy.

MISS LAURA
> You ever see Spirit Blood, Doctah?

JEB LUCAS
> I seen plenty a blood in my day.

MISS LAURA
> Ah ain't talkin' bout no human blood. We gots to go down there tonight! You wanna live…you better come on.

JEB LUCAS

I'll be in Columbia tonight.

MISS LAURA

Spirit don't know time or place…only the scent of de human it touch.

CHICKEN LEG

Ya seen her! Didn't ya! Ya seen de African!

WATAH MOCASIN

Ah didn't see nothin'!

Drums come up as the sky changes color. Voice of Mean Molly cries out:

VOICE OF MEAN MOLLY

E si ye mo le.

Miss Laura puts her hands to the sky.

VOICE OF MEAN MOLLY

Nwon ni ki o ru!

Drums rise in intensity.

MISS LAURA

It de African spirit. Watah Mocasin's blood make her so strong she out de graveyard. Ya gots her blood on yoh hand, Doctah!

VOICE OF MEAN MOLLY

O ni ki o pe!

JEB LUCAS

(Grabbing his suitcase) I'm heading out! I ain't got no business with witches!

MISS LAURA

She was Yoruba! Not a witch!

VOICE OF MEAN MOLLY

Obonto!

MISS LAURA

The African spirit of a slave that wouldn't die.

CHICKEN LEG

What ts mean Mama?

MISS LAURA

Sacrifice.

SIX
Miss Laura cooks up a plan

Main Man runs in.

MAIN MAN
Grandma! Something wrong.

MISS LAURA
Where brother?

MAIN MAN
In de field. Lyin' there. He can't move, Daddy.

CHICKEN LEG
Lord have mercy.

MAIN MAN
Hurry. Ba Ba 'bout to die.

MISS LAURA
Hush your mouth. Don't speak 'bout no dyin'.

CHICKEN LEG
Something happen to Ba Ba, it on you Mocasin.

MISS LAURA
We ain't got time for all that!

Baby Brother limps in.

MAIN MAN
Here come Baby Brother right here.

CHICKEN LEG
You alright, son?

BABY BROTHER
Something out there, Daddy.

MISS LAURA
What happen, Ba Ba?

BABY BROTHER
I was layin' out seed in the South field. Something knock me down!

MAIN MAN
He just lay there like a dead man!

VOICE OF MEAN MOLLY
Obonto!

Drums begin to rage.

MISS LAURA

(To Chicken Leg) Go find de Preacher. Then get you 9 buckets a watah. Tell de Preacher he gone need ta lay his hands on dat watah.

CHICKEN LEG

Come on, boys.

MISS LAURA

Watah Mocasin…you go up to de smokehouse.

WATAH MOCASIN

Massah George smokehouse?

MISS LAURA

Dat where she die.

WATAH MOCASIN

Ain't been up dere since it happen.

MISS LAURA

Well..you goin' today.

WATAH MOCASIN

Why Ah ever go down to that graveyard hole?

MISS LAURA

Go inside. To de back corner. On de right. Scoop up some a dat dirt. Bring it to me.

VOICE OF MEAN MOLLY

O ni ki o pe!

Watah Mocasin runs off.

MISS LAURA

Massah George bought him a spirit he couldn't tame.
Ah hears ya. Dey should a never brought ya 'cross dat ocean.

Miss Laura remembers the day Mean Molly arrived.

SEVEN
African slave days

Massah George thrusts Mean Molly onstage.

MASSAH GEORGE

Get over there. You ain't getting' no shack, bed, food, 'til you start working.

MEAN MOLLY

Obonto!

MASSAH GEORGE

Shut up with all that. You 'bout as mean and lazy as my mule. Good name for ya. We gone call this African…Mean Molly.

MEAN MOLLY
Nwon ni ki o ru.

MASSAH GEORGE
This South Carolina. Speak English!

MEAN MOLLY
OBONTO!

African drums begin to rage.

MASSAH GEORGE
(To Miss Laura) Get her to eat!

Massah George quickly leaves. Miss Laura crosses to Mean Molly with a bowl of food.

MISS LAURA
Mark of a Yoruba on yoh face. Scarification mark of beauty. You got to eat, gal.

Mean Molly hurls the bowl across the ground.

MEAN MOLLY
Nwon ni ki!

MISS LAURA
Massah George gone kill you!

MEAN MOLLY
Obonto!

MISS LAURA
What you be sayin'?

MEAN MOLLY
Obonto.

Obonto appears through the mist.

MISS LAURA
Lord. Who is that? Look like an African king.

OBONTO
Watch over my child.

MISS LAURA
What is you?

OBONTO
Obonto.

MISS LAURA
You de one she cryin' foh?

OBONTO
Daughter of Shango!

MISS LAURA
My Daddy was a slave.

OBONTO
Daughter of Shango!

MISS LAURA
Been gone a long time.

OBONTO
He watch you.

MISS LAURA
From where?

OBONTO
The Ancestor house.

MISS LAURA
What are you?

OBONTO
Ijebu.

MISS LAURA
'N her?

OBONTO
A West African that must return.

MEAN MOLLY
OBONTO!

Drums rise as Mean Molly runs to Obonto as he fades into the mist. She falls to the ground.

MISS LAURA
That was the day I saw love so strong…the spirit left the body to get back to where it belong.

EIGHT
Getting' ready for the smokehouse.

Chicken Leg, Main Man, Baby Brother enter.

CHICKEN LEG
Them hams ready for the smokehouse?

MISS LAURA
Ah'ma gettin' to 'em.

CHICKEN LEG
Massah George want 'em up there now!

MAIN MAN
Why she just lay there, Grandma?

MISS LAURA
She sick.

BABY BROTHER
Massah George gone beat you!

MEAN MOLLY
Nwon ni ki!

MAIN MAN
She better get to work!

MISS LAURA
She ain't never gone be no slave.

MAIN MAN
She already a slave.

MISS LAURA
Dis look like something Massah George own?

BABY BROTHER
He gone put her in a grave!

MISS LAURA
Massah George do what he got ta do.

CHICKEN LEG
Been 3 year since he sold Cora. Why don't you eat, gal?

MEAN MOLLY
Obonto!

MISS LAURA
She ain't gonna eat.

CHICKEN LEG
Ah needs me a wife.

MISS LAURA
Don't be thinkin' 'bout this gal.

CHICKEN LEG
She be strong if she eat.

MISS LAURA
Dis gals spirit ain't here.

CHICKEN LEG
What you mean?

MISS LAURA

Don't be thinkin' bout this gal.

CHICKEN LEG

Can't sit here and watch her die. You gonna eat.

Chicken Leg grabs a bowl of mush from Miss Laura's table, thrusts his hands in it, and shoves a handful of food into Mean Molly's mouth. She spits it out and tries to bite Chicken Leg.

MISS LAURA

This ain't yoh business.

MEAN MOLLY

Obonto!

CHICKEN LEG

You a mean woman.

MEAN MOLLY

Obonto!

Voice of Massah George is heard shouting:

VOICE OF MASSAH GEORGE

You got my hams ready?

MISS LAURA

Ah'ma dressing 'em.

VOICE OF MASSAH GEORGE

Bring that gal up to the smokehouse with my hams, Chicken Leg.

CHICKEN LEG

What gal that be, Massah?

VOICE OF MASSAH GEORGE

That African.

CHICKEN LEG

She too sick to move, Massah.

VOICE OF MASSAH GEORGE

Oh she gone move. I'm gone burn that bad blood outa her.

CHICKEN LEG

Yes sir, Massah. Sure will bring them hams and the gal.

Chicken Leg looks around forming a plan.

CHICKEN LEG

Gone take her down to the waterhole.

MISS LAURA

You understand what he sayin'?

MEAN MOLLY
Nwon ni ki.

CHICKEN LEG
Massah George aim to kill you!

MISS LAURA
Might be weeks 'fore we could move her out.

CHICKEN LEG
Better she die by the waterhole than in the smokehouse.

MISS LAURA
African spirit! What you want us to do with your gal?

Obonto appears through the mist.

OBONTO
The man who steals what is not for sale…dies.

MISS LAURA
Take her to the smokehouse.

CHICKEN LEG
He gone burn here with 'dem hams.

MISS LAURA
Take her!

OBONTO
Fire that burns of ham…rots with flesh.

MISS LAURA
Go on. Take her.

CHICKEN LEG
What wrong with you?

MISS LAURA
I said take her. Now go on. Be done with it.

VOICE OF MASSAH GEORGE
I want them hams 'n that African now, Chicken Leg. Them pecans roasting brown.

CHICKEN LEG
Here I come.

OBONTO
Nomikonto!

Mean Molly rises up as she hears her name.

OBONTO
Go with this man.

MEAN MOLLY

(Refusing) Ni oro won.

OBONTO

Listen to me, woman!

MEAN MOLLY

Ni oro won.

OBONTO

(Commanding her) Prepare yourself.

MEAN MOLLY

(Bows her head in obedience) Obonto.

NINE
Murder in the Smokehouse

Drumming. Obonto appears inside the smokehouse.

OBONTO

Ifa says there is a woman. A woman of noble birth.
There was a hog farmer. The hog farmer had never seen a woman.
The hog farmer knew the price of hogs. Gold cannot buy a woman.
The eye of the hog farmer must sacrifice.

MASSAH GEORGE

Get over here. These hams smoke twelve hours. Let's see how long it gonna take to smoke Africa out of you.

OBONTO

Hog farmer.

MASSAH GEORGE

Keep your mouth shut 'til I get you tied.

OBONTO

Hog farmer cannot see to tie a rope.

MASSAH GEORGE

Can't see in here.

OBONTO

Hog farmer touches the queen with unclean hands.

MASSAH GEORGE

Lord, my hands is burning up.

OBONTO

Hog farmer does not stand on the legs of a man.

Massah George falls to the ground.

MASSAH GEORGE

    (To Mean Molly) You kick me? I'll kill ya right here!

Massah George plunges a knife into Mean Molly's stomach.

OBONTO

    (Enraged) Hog farmer must sacrifice!

MASSAH GEORGE

    I can't move. I can't see anything. Chicken Leg!

OBONTO

    Hog farmer speaks. No Yoruba answers.

MASSAH GEORGE

    Chicken Leg, get in here! My eyes is burnin'!

OBONTO

    Hog farmer will never own the daughter of Obonto!

MASSAH GEORGE

    Ahhhhchickenleg…chick..en…leg….ahhhh

Fumbling around in the dark, Chicken Leg enters.

CHICKEN LEG

    Massah George? You ahright? Lord have mercy! What kind a smell in here? Massah George?

OBONTO

    The hog farmer is before the elders.

CHICKEN LEG

    What wrong, Massah? Dang! Where dat stink coming from?

OBONTO

    The flesh of the hog farmer.

CHICKEN LEG

    Massah George, you betta' get up and come on out a here. Massah. Is you dead? Praise God Almighty! Is you dead? Where is you, gal?

MEAN MOLLY

    (Faint dying whisper) Obonto.

CHICKEN LEG

    Lord have mercy. Is ya dead? You done kill Massah George. Massah George done kill you.

Chicken Leg bows his troubled head.

OBONTO

    Shango!

Drums respond to his call

OBONTO

    100 years from now. Obatala!

100 years from now. Ogun!
Ancestors speak. Children listen. Africa. Remembered.

Drums rage into the dark blueness of the mystic.

TEN
Preacher comes to bless the buckets

Miss Laura anxiously awaits Chicken Leg. Main Man and Baby Brother enter with buckets in each hand, followed by Preacher, who immediately takes charge of the situation.

MISS LAURA
Where yoh Daddy?

BABY BROTHER
Preacher sent him to the creek.

PREACHER
Got to have fresh water from the creek, Miss Laura.

MISS LAURA
She out de graveyard, Preacher.

PREACHER
And on the third day He arose.

MISS LAURA
She angry, Preacher.

PREACHER
My people been angry long time in South Carolina.

MISS LAURA
Ya gots ta help her.

PREACHER
That's why I come.

MAIN MAN
You gone bless the water?

PREACHER
How many ya gots there, Baby Brother?

BABY BROTHER
Two full buckets, Preacher.

PREACHER
Main Man?

MAIN MAN
Got two but this one ain't but half.

PREACHER

Gots to have nine! Got to wait on yoh Daddy!

MISS LAURA

I tole them bring nine buckets!

BABY BROTHER

Why you gots to have nine?

PREACHER

Cause we aim to send that African home! Gone set her free. Praise His Name!

MISS LAURA

Amen!

Watah Mocasin enters in a trance.

WATAH MOCASIN

You shouldn't a sent me up there, Miss Laura.

(Falls down as if dead)

PREACHER

Stay back!

BABY BROTHER

He dead?

MISS LAURA

Spirit blood gone inside him!

PREACHER

What he holdin'?

MISS LAURA

Smokehouse dirt.

MAIN MAN

She kill Massah George up there.

PREACHER

Boy! We ain't here to be talking about all that. Them sins past. Let 'em go.

Jeb Lucas enters in a trance.

JEB LUCAS

She took my paper. Floated up on the road. Stood there. In the tree!

PREACHER

Where'd he come from?

MAIN MAN

He the doctor.

BABY BROTHER

He be fixin' Daddy's leg.

JEB LUCAS

I got papers! You see my papers? I was a Union soldier. Sewed up cats and tails...arms.... Don't come near me!

PREACHER

Stay back, children!

Jeb Lucas saunters around in a crazed circle, muttering to himself.

CHICKEN LEG

Got you five buckets a fresh water from the creek, Preacher.

PREACHER

Stay back, Chicken Leg.

JEB LUCAS

Blood come on my hands like cherry water. Wasn't medicine. I'm Jeb Liquor from, Ohio, Michigan, Tennesee...where did I get born? Them black eyes came out of the tree and jumped on my hand. Her face come up on my hand. Get away from me!

PREACHER

Noone gonna hurt you, son.

JEB LUCAS

General Sherman! She come off my hand like blood dancing. Drums were coming outa my head and she called...

Mean Molly runs across the playing area.

MOLLY MEANS

Obonto!

WATAH MOCASIN

(Rising) Nwon ni ki o ru!

PREACHER

Father be with us now. Let us pray! We got some troubled folks in Gullah county today. I say, we got troubled folks in South Carolina. Gots ta clean the spirit of this land.

ALL

Clean the spirit of this land.

PREACHER

Gots to wash yoh back, Watah Mocasin.

ALL

Clean the spirit of this land.

PREACHER

Gots to wash de blood off yoh hands, doctah.

ALL

Amen!

JEB LUCAS

I ain't goin to no church.

WATAH MOCASIN

Don't be layin' yoh hands on me.

PREACHER

Watah Mocasin. You in there?

WATAH MOCASIN

Fish hungy.

PREACHER

He still floating around behind them eyes.

WATAH MOCASIN

They weren't bitin' by the lake, Preacher.

PREACHER

You was hungry?

WATAH MOCASIN

Uh hum.

PREACHER

Ah'ma putting my hands over this water. I say! Ah'ma putting my hands over this water. Put the cleansing in my hands. Let the spirit clean the water!

ALL

Clean the water!

PREACHER

Come to me, Mocasin.

WATAH MOCASIN

You ain't Massah George is ya?

PREACHER

You know me. Preacher. Now come on over here. Ya'll bring them buckets to the circle.

Ensemble forms a circle around Jeb Lucas and Watah Mocasin. Mean Molly reappears as the drums begin to call her home.

MEAN MOLLY

E si ye mo le !

WATAH MOCASIN

That's her. The one come on my back!

JEB LUCAS

Don't come up on my hand! Get her off me, General Sherman!

PREACHER

You gots to come to me!

JEB LUCAS

I ain't gonna surrender to no Confederate.

PREACHER

I'm a Union soldier, just like you. Come over here.

Jeb Lucas comes inside the circle. Mean Molly gyrates into the circle crying out.

MEAN MOLLY

E si ye mo le!

PREACHER

We gots nine buckets a holy water. We gots two troubled men. We gots a dead African that died in Massah George smokehouse. We asking to set this African free.

ALL

Set her free, Lord.

PREACHER

Let her go home. She can't get home in no slave grave.

ALL

Can't get home.

PREACHER

Let the fresh water turn to salt water. Let the ocean claim her soul. Mother Africa take your daughter home!

Preacher raises his bucket of water, all follow, nine buckets of water are poured on the backs of Jeb Lucas and Watah Mocasin.

ELEVEN
Spirit Cleansing for the Journey Home

Sounds of the mystic ocean transform the sky to a midnight blue.

PREACHER

Time for you two mens to stand on your truth.

CROWD

Testify!

PREACHER

Your souls are cleansed.

CROWD

Testify!

WATAH MOCASIN

I went down to that graveyard hole…I sure did.

PREACHER

How many Africans buried down there, Mocasin?

WATAH MOCASIN

Don't know.

MISS LAURA

That was a slave camp, boy.

PREACHER

Slave camp where they broke the spirit.

CROWD

Broke the spirit!

PREACHER

Plenty Africans never got to no plantation. West Africans they couldn't break!

CROWD

Testify!

PREACHER

What you gone do with a West African won't be no slave?

CROWD

Put 'em in a grave.

PREACHER

Nothing but Africans buried down by that waterhole. Ain't no place to go fishing!

WATAH MOCASIN:

Aint never gonna disrespect the dead. Never again.

PREACHER

What about you, doctor?

JEB LUCAS

I ain't a real doctor.

MISS LAURA

I tole you that man wasn't no doctor.

CHICKEN LEG

Already knew that, Mama.

JEB LUCAS

How you know that?

CHICKEN LEG

Cause I read those army discharge papers you carry around.

CROWD

Testify!

JEB LUCAS

Learning a lot about being a man today. Learning you got to respect your fellow man.

PREACHER

Walk out of the circle and stand tall, my brothers.

African drums come up. Obanto appears through the mist. The people see and hear the presence of Africa.

PREACHER

African spirit. I'm coming to you as a son of Africa. How do we bring this gal home?

OBONTO

Sacrifice.

CHICKEN LEG

We gots to sacrifice our understanding of Mean Molly.

WATAH MOCASIN

I been hearing her cries out by the graveyeard for ten years.

CHICKEN LEG

I been seeing that gal as a dead slave for ten years.

MISS LAURA

See the gal as she was. Ijebu.

CHICKEN LEG

Nomikonto. A princess of West Africa.

PREACHER

We return your trust to the Ancestor House.

Nomikonto appears in her native dress. The crowd bows in reverence.

OBONTO

The Ancestors sat at the table in Mother Africa.
Elders, who had come for the knowledge.
The Great Spirit gave each a Tablet.
Hold the mystery!
Guardians of Water.
The Warrior Kings would build kingdoms.
Igboland, Benin, Dahomey, Senegambia, Hausaland, Yorubaland
Portuguese, British, Spanish, French, Dutch,
Came to West Africa.
They came from the kings of Europe,
To sit with the kings of Africa,
That all men might remember the Ancient Mystery.

Drums rage, returning Nomikonto to the Ancestors. The playing area is transformed into the deep blue of the mystic ocean.

Fade to Black as the drums continue.

End of Play

Let Thy Last Word Be Freedom

Denmark Vesey & the Insurrection of 1822

Dramatized for the stage by Carolyn Nur Wistrand

*Multiple Roles for

10 Males

5 Females

*All speaking roles are for African American youth except for Captain Vesey and Judge Hamilton.

CHARACTERS

THE CARRIBEAN (1786)	CHARLESTON (1800-1822)
Night Spirit	Beck
Island Spirits	Tuesday
Young Denmark	Peter Poyas
Euphrates	Monday Gell
Captain Vesey	Rolla Bennett
Enslaved African Men	Denmark Vesey
	Ned Bennett
	Captain Vesey
	Mingo Harth
	Batteau Bennett
	Gullah Jack
	George Wilson
	Market Women
	Judge Hamilton

SCENE ONE
St. Thomas, Virgin Islands, West Indies
1786

The crashing of waves against the island shore is heard as the dark blue/black of midnight illuminates the bare stage. Night Spirit, covered in white dust, is discerned kneeling at the shore's edge. Reaching down he scoops a handful of sand into his palms and brings it close to his face as the Island Spirits arrive.

NIGHT SPIRIT
(Tasting the sand)
What vision forms from the taste on my tongue of land not free?
Night Season!
Cover forever the stalks of sugar made sweet by stolen Africans.
Ebony velvet rides the memory of day not long enough to escape this
Virgin Island,
stained in blood.

ISLAND SPIRITS
Hidden on sweet grass far from this shore,
his body knows rest, from us ask no more!

NIGHT SPIRIT
Omnipotent God creates man and will,
To walk his destiny, the boy must prepare.

ISLAND SPIRITS
We dance in his dreams, his body so lean,
The milk of our breasts, we beg…let him seek.

NIGHT SPIRIT
Cover yourselves! No babe awakens this night.
Your desire for earthly passion, keeps the boy on ocean spirit.
Look out there! The Slaver has cast out her burden this night!

ISLAND SPIRITS
Seven and twenty drop to the ocean's floor!

NIGHT SPIRIT
Is this your desire for the lean boy?

ISLAND SPIRITS
He sleeps in peace!

NIGHT SPIRIT
He wakes in chains!

ISLAND SPIRITS
Our mystery heals his sorrow.

NIGHT SPIRIT
The ship arrives on this island with dawn!

Into the belly of the Bermuda trader…three hundred and ninety will be thrown.

ISLAND SPIRITS

His journey with us ends with this moon?

NIGHT SPIRIT

Call him up!

ISLAND SPIRITS

We place our hands on silent space, soul of lean boy, swim into grace.

Young Denmark comes forth in a dream state. Island Spirits circle the young boy as Spirit of Night majestically reveals knowledge for his safe passing.

NIGHT SPIRIT

Hear then boy of courageous heart,
A drop of truth, your destiny on earth.
Stay in silence when the slaver's hand,
Breaks you in chains, stalks at your man.
The axe of Shango shall guide you by day and night.
Listen to ancient drums in thunder!
Grow as steadfast as the oak!
Freedom,
I place it low in your soul,
As seed to the soil,
Eternal it shall grow.

YOUNG DENMARK

(From deep within his subconscious the boy cries out)
FREEDOM!

ISLAND SPIRITS

Be Thy Last Word!

NIGHT SPIRIT

Return to the village. The Ancestors are appeased.

Young Denmark leaves the presence of the Spirits as thunder breaks through the sky. Night Spirit raises his hands to the Spirit World, the Island Spirits fade into the blue mist as dawn beckons.

SCENE TWO
St. Thomas, Virgin Islands, Dutch West Indies

Early the next morning.

Offstage sound of uniform stomping summon the arrival of the Slaver. Offstage voices are heard:

SEAFARING CREW
>LAND ASHORE!!

1ST CREWMAN
>ANCHORS DOWN!

2ND CREWMAN
>SECURE THE MAST!

3RD CREWMAN
>TALLY HO!

4TH CREWMAN
>SEAL THE WINDLASS!

5TH CREWMAN
>SHE'S SECURE CAPTAIN!

6TH CREWMAN
>WEIGH ANCHOR.

Captain Vesey, a Dutch Sea Captain of the late 1700's now comes forward attired in a red velvet jacket, white lace shirt, knickers, white tights, and a leather strap across his chest, from which two pistols protrude. From his elaborate red and black velvet hat his long ponytail falls down his back. He speaks to his crew.

CAPTAIN VESEY
>Get that rum out of the holds. Euphrates!

Euphrates rushes in.

EUPHRATES
>Captain Vesey.

CAPTAIN VESEY
>I want them chained below the hatch by noon.

EUPHRATES
>Sir.

CAPTAIN VESEY
>I expect a good profit on this cargo. *(Spitting)* Won't bring a dime if they got the fits.

EUPHRATES
>Sir.

CAPTAIN VESEY
>Get 'em on board!

Euphrates runs to the holding pen, offstage, slashing his whip he moves a group of bare-chested African men, chained together, onto the ship.

EUPHRATES
MOVE!

The Enslaved African Men enter in unison, backs bent, heads low. They stand on the deck of ship and turn out crying:

ENSLAVED AFRICAN MEN
Obatala!

Euphrates begins examining men as they talk amongst themselves. Captain Vesey, who can't understand their language, smokes his pipe examining the men as cargo.

ENSLAVED AFRICAN MAN
Where is he taking us?

ENSLAVED AFRICAN ELDER
To his country.

ENSLAVED AFRICAN MAN
To eat us?

ENSLAVED AFRICAN ELDER
To work in the big cane fields.

CAPTAIN VESEY
(With no human regard for the men, examines them as merchandise, checking off items on his list.)
Look to be in good shape, hair seem healthy enough?

EUPHRATES
Yes Sir!

CAPTAIN VESEY
No film over the eyes?

EUPHRATES
No sir!

CAPTAIN VESEY
Show your teeth!

ENSLAVED AFRICAN MAN
What is this White Devil saying?

CAPTAIN VESEY
Get their mouths open!

EUPHRATES
(Slashing his whip on the floor of the ship) Open your mouths!

Enslaved Africans show their teeth in a disgruntled manner as Captain Vesey walks in front of them.

EUPHRATES

(Noticing one man will not open his mouth.) This one don't seem to understand you, Captain.

CAPTAIN VESEY

(Walks up to the African whose lips remain sealed, takes out his gun and points it at the man's mouth.) You understand this?

ENSLAVED AFRICAN MAN

Uhmmm.

ENSLAVED AFRICAN ELDER

Open, man before he shoots!

ENSLAVED AFRICAN

(As Euphrates shoves his mouth open) Curse you, rotten fish belly!

CAPTAIN VESEY

Savages with such fine pearl. Get 'em to jump.

EUPHRATES

(Euphrates walks down the line of men whipping their feet so they will jump.) Jump!

CAPTAIN VESEY

Should bring me a fortune in Charleston. Throw 'em in the hold.

Euphrates leads the men below. The stench of the lower deck fills the nostrils of the enslaved men. They moan, gasp for air, cough, and dry heave.

ENSLAVED AFRICAN MAN

(Coughing) Where is this?

Men continue to cough and gag from stench below as Vesey commands from above deck.

CAPTAIN VESEY

Shackle those ankles right left.

ENSLAVED AFRICAN MAN

He gone to kill us down here?

ENSLAVED AFRICAN ELDER

Save your strength.

ENSLAVED AFRICAN MAN

I can't breathe.

EUPHRATES

(With a hammer) Feet together.

ENSLAVED AFRICAN MAN

He goes to cut our feet off!

ENSLAVED AFRICAN ELDER

Patience, man.

EUPHRATES
(Calling above to Captain) They all secure, Captain.

CAPTAIN VESEY
(Calling below to Euphrates) Get 'em fed before we sail.

EUPHRATES
These yams full of worms, Captain.

CAPTAIN VESEY
Pick 'em off.

EUPHRATES
Yes sir, Captain Vesey. *(Picking worms off yams)*

ENSLAVED AFRICAN MAN
No!

ENSLAVED AFRICAN MAN
I can't eat that!

ENSLAVED AFRICAN MAN
Obatala!

African men rattle the chains.

EUPHRATES
They won't eat, Captain.

CAPTAIN VESEY
Shoot the smallest one.

Chains rattle with rising intensity as Euphrates takes out his pistol and points it at the head of young Denmark.

ENSLAVED AFRICAN ELDER
EAT, MAN. EAT!!

EUPHRATES
They got hungry.

Euphrates quickly shoves yams into the mouths of the men. The men gag and spit the rotten food out.

ENSLAVED AFRICAN ELDER
Swallow before he kills the boy!

CAPTAIN VESEY
Scoop out some of that fresh water.

EUPHRATES
Hate to waste it on savages.

CAPTAIN VESEY
Dead Africans ain't worth a drink of salt water!

EUPHRATES

Yes sir!

He rapidly scoops a ladle into a bucket of fresh water; the men greedily drink.

ENSLAVED AFRICAN ELDER

Drink it slow!

CAPTAIN VESEY

Finish up down there I want to move ahead of this storm.

EUPHRATES

(Running on deck) Ready, Captain!

CAPTAIN VESEY

God speed us to South Carolina!

ENSLAVED AFRICAN MEN

Coolness of night cover us!

SCENE THREE
The Voyage
Caribbean to Atlantic

The ocean sounds turn into the sounds of thunder as the ship begins its course to South Carolina. The Africans in the hatch violently sway as the waves hit the ship. Captain Vesey enters the deck and looks out across the ocean through his spyglass. Euphrates walks the deck pulling masts into line. The Night Spirit and Island Spirits journey with the ship as background movement. The effect should be of a sea voyage, rocking, crashing, and colliding through continual movement. When Captain Vesey calls for his dinner, the Africans in the hatch continue to rock in full view of the audience.

CAPTAIN VESEY

(Coming forward) Euphrates! My dinner! *(Euphrates enters with a rolling cart, elegantly covered with white tablecloth, silver covered plates and a bottle of wine. Vesey stands holding up the plate cover as Euphrates brings in a red velvet chair for him. Vesey sits and bows his head for prayer.)* Heavenly father, bless this food that you have bountifully given me, *(Shouting at Euphrates)* close your eyes during prayer, boy!

ENSLAVED AFRICAN MAN

(Rocking in languid movement) What does he do up there?

ENSLAVED AFRICAN MAN

Prays for God to make him rich.

ENSLAVED AFRICAN MAN

Marks us in his book. Dog 1, Dog 2, Dog Dead.

ENSLAVED AFRICAN MAN

God has abandoned us!

AFRICAN ELDER
Quiet! This is the work of man, not God!

CAPTAIN VESEY
(Putting his napkin below his chin he cuts his food)
Did you shoot the small one?

EUPHRATES
They all ate, Captain.

CAPTAIN VESEY
I could use a new cabin boy. *(Taking a bite of food)* Get him up here.

Euphrates runs below and unshackles young Denmark.

ENSLAVED AFRICAN MAN
He comes for the boy!

EUPHRATES
(Shoving Young Denmark up the hatch) Captain wants you on deck.

YOUNG DENMARK
No!

AFRICAN ELDER
Courage, boy!

ENSLAVED AFRICAN MAN
Better to die above.

ENSLAVED AFRICAN MEN
Obatala!

Euphrates brings young Denmark to the Captains table, as Captain pours himself a glass of wine.

CAPTAIN VESEY
Turn him around.

EUPHRATES
(Motioning with his hand) Spin!

Young Denmark rapidly spins.

CAPTAIN VESEY
(Drinking from his wineglass) Slower!

Young Denmark spins slower.

CAPTAIN VESEY
So, you understand me.

YOUNG DENMARK
I understand you.

EUPHRATES
Not a mark on him, Captain Vesey.

CAPTAIN VESEY

Good. *(Pointing to a drum in his cabin)* Can you beat the drum?

YOUNG DENMARK

I know many drums.

CAPTAIN VESEY

Perhaps I shall keep you. Fetch him some clothes.

Euphrates runs off as Young Denmark looks around the cabin.

CAPTAIN VESEY

It's civilization you see here. The great Western civilization.

YOUNG DENMARK

Made rich by Africa?

CAPTAIN VESEY

Made rich by God! I was born a man. You were born a savage.

EUPHRATES

(Returning with a jacket) This should fit him, Captain.

CAPTAIN VESEY

Dress him. You shall be my cabin boy. Maps on the table at dawn. My spyglass cleaned each night at 8. You sleep by the door.

EUPHRATES

What will you call him, Captain Vesey?

CAPTAIN VESEY

(Taking his napkin from his neck he stands up) I shall call him Telemaque.

EUPHRATES

Why not just Denmark, sir.

CAPTAIN VESEY

(Throwing a large turkey bone on the floor.) Telemaque… Denmark, what's the difference?

Captain leaves the area as Euphrates rolls the table out. Young Denmark falls to the floor and holds his head.

ISLAND SPIRITS

Telemaque!

ENSLAVED AFRICAN MEN

Denmark!

ISLAND SPIRITS

Telemaque!

EUPHRATES

(Shoving a broom at him) Denmark!

Young Denmark jumps up and begins to sweep floor, wash off table, put on maps, clean spyglass.

ISLAND SPIRITS

Like a serpent ever coiling, in a tale of hells descent,
the life of Denmark Vesey as a cabin boy now was spent.

CAPTAIN VESEY

Bring 'em up, Euphrates! Dance those slaves, Denmark!

Euphrates quickly brings the Africans on deck as Young Denmark stands with his broom, hitting the deck in a pathetic rhythm the African men must dance to as Euphrates hits their feet with the whip.

EUPHRATES

Dance, you dogs!

Night Spirit comes forward as Africans continue to slovenly move as Euphrates continues to whip their feet.

ISLAND SPIRITS

And he watched a mighty nation,
Proclaiming,
All men are created free,
Strip the souls of Africans,
Of their pride and dignity.

NIGHT SPIRIT

Hatred into Denmark was now truly born.
He belonged to the Slave Captain.

CAPTAIN VESEY

Euphrates! Denmark! Oil 'em down.

Young Denmark and Euphrates grab two buckets and rub oil onto the chests of the Africans from the buckets.

EUPHRATES

Why don't you ever talk, boy?

YOUNG DENMARK VESEY

I do my job.

EUPHRATES

They gonna make the Captain a fine profit at The Auction House.

CAPTAIN VESEY

Head 'em out.

EUPHRATES

Move!

The chained men move offstage.

CAPTAIN VESEY

Denmark! Get that hold scrubbed out! Soon as I get 'em sold we'll be bringing fresh rum on board. I don't want it stinkin!

Young Denmark jumps down into the hatch and mops the floor, as Captain Vesey smokes his pipe. The Island Spirits enter.

ISLAND SPIRITS

Aboard the mighty Slaver, the Triangular Trade, their route to roam.

NIGHT SPIRIT

AFRICA...CARIBBEAN...CHARLESTON.

ISLAND SPIRITS

To capture, break and sell Africans, Captain Vesey prayed each night.

CAPTAIN VESEY

Heavenly Father. Watch over this ship that no harm comes on this voyage.

ISLAND SPIRITS

The Captain taught his first mate the same prayer!

EUPHRATES

Please Lord, let Captain Vesey get him a good cargo a Black gold. And let me get mine. That's all Lord...please let me get mine.

From offstage the crew yells out:

CREW 1

HURL THE MAST!

CREW 2

BRING UP THOSE ANCHORS!

CREW 3

HANDS ON DECK!

CREW 4

TALLY HO!

CREW

SET SAIL FOR THE GOLD COAST!

ISLAND SPIRITS

With a belly full of rum and trinkets, the serpent slaver sled. All for the price of rum!

Euphrates crossing down to Young Denmark in the hold.

EUPHRATES

(Pen and chart in hand) You count that rum?

YOUNG DENMARK

One thousand barrels.

EUPHRATES

You a hundred short.

YOUNG DENMARK

That's what was loaded.

EUPHRATES

Count 'em again! We gonna lose thirty savages in the trade.

YOUNG DENMARK

How's that?

EUPHRATES

It takes 3 barrels to buy an African. Captain, ready to trade!

Drums are heard as Night Spirit now commands African tribesmen to enter as Island Spirits dance in swirling movements around them.

NIGHT SPIRIT

Mandingo!

Enslaved African man rushes onboard.

NIGHT SPIRIT

Igbo!

Two enslaved African men rush onboard.

NIGHT SPIRIT

Yoruba!

Two enslaved African men rush onboard.

NIGHT SPIRIT

Senegalese!

Enslaved African man rushes onboard.

NIGHT SPIRIT

Angolese!

Enslaved African man rushes onboard.

NIGHT SPIRIT

Congolese!

Three enslaved African men rush onboard.

ISLAND SPIRITS

From the soul of Mother Africa, Captain's Vesey's blood was fed.

CAPTAIN VESEY

Put 'em in the hold, Euphrates!

Drums begin to rage as Euphrates shoves men in the hold; Night Spirit and Island Spirits begin to move to the drums.

NIGHT SPIRIT

AFRICA!

ISLAND SPIRITS

CARIBBEAN!

ENSLAVED AFRICAN MEN
> CHARLESTON!

NIGHT SPIRIT
> AFRICA!

ISLAND SPIRITS
> CARIBBEAN!

ENSLAVED AFRICAN MEN
> CHARLESTON!

NIGHT SPIRIT
> AFRICA!

ISLAND SPIRITS
> CARIBBEAN!

ENSLAVED AFRICAN MEN
> CHARLESTON!

> *Now in a faint whisper, whirling in slow motion.*

ENSLAVED AFRICAN MEN/ISLAND SPIRITS/NIGHT SPIRIT
> Africa….Caribbean…Charleston.

> *As the drums continue, the enslaved African men rhythmically leave the boat; Night Spirit and Island Spirit return to the Ancestral Realms.*

SCENE FOUR
Charleston, South Carolina
1800

Beck enters with a basket of cotton on her head. Additional women enter with baskets, kneeling to pick cotton.

BECK
> Broken bits of humanity,
> strewn like cotton balls bleedin',
> on the tips of dark hands.
> Up and down the Carolina coast,
> And we were waitin'.
> Waitin' to remember,
> the sound of the mother tongue.
> To bless our newborn.
> Waitin to remember,
> The sacred name of God.
> They called us now to Jesus….and we were waitin' for Him.

TUESDAY
> *(Running in)* Beck! Your man, he just bought his freedom!

BECK

Massa Barker wants a good price on this cotton. You clean that sample rice good?

TUESDAY

I'm talking about Denmark Vesey just won the lottery! Fifteen Hundred dollars! Everybody talkin' about it up and down the wharf!

BECK

What's that got to do with me? Pick that rice clean 'fore Massa put you back in the field!

TUESDAY

He gone buy your freedom sure enough!

BECK

He got's to buy his own first don't he?

TUESDAY

He gone up to see the Captain.

BECK

We gots five more bushels to bring in.

TUESDAY

You ain't heard a word I said.

BECK

I heard your words and I know my truth.

TUESDAY

Beck…

BECK

I have born that man 3 sons. Not one of them belongs to Denmark…Massa Barker will never let me and mines go.

Beck leaves.

Peter Poyas comes forth, and talks directly to the audience as Ned, Rolla, and Monday Gell enter with carpentry tools and begin to put siding on a imaginary house.

PETER POYAS

Worked as a carpenter side by side with Denmark Vesey for thirty-four years.

MONDAY GELL

Knew him seventeen years… giving his daily wage to the ole Captain

NED BENNETT

Knew him the next seventeen putting that wage in his own bank account.

PETER POYAS

In between the enslaved and the freed stood my brother, Denmark.

MONDAY GELL

Black free man nothing more than a ex-slave in Charleston.

ROLLA BENNETT

What that suppose to mean?

MONDAY GELL

He gonna find out what he already know.

PETER POYAS

Charleston had many kinds of identification tags in 1800.

MONDAY GELL

You got the field slaves working rice and cotton down by the swamps.

NED BENNETT

Me and Rolla here, work for the Governor, what they tag the city house slaves.

ROLLA BENNETT

We could walk in his bedroom any night of the week and slit his throat.

PETER POYAS

(Rising intensity towards the others) I am here talking about the hired out wage on the day Denmark went up to see the Captain!

Men go back to work as Denmark and Captain come forward.

PETER POYAS

It was the last day of the 18th century. He handed the Captain six hundred dollars for his manumission papers.

Denmark hands Captain Vesey six hundred dollars.

CAPTAIN VESEY

(Counting the money) Your the best hired out city slave I've ever owned.

DENMARK VESEY

It's all there.

CAPTAIN VESEY

Hundred dollar bills?

DENMARK VESEY

Six of them.

CAPTAIN VESEY

Who would of ever thought you'd be holding that kind of money?

DENMARK VESEY

You need to sign and date the paper, sir.

CAPTAIN VESEY

What you gonna do with the rest of that? *(Handing the papers to Denmark)*

DENMARK VESEY

I have some plans. *(Handing him his identification slave tag)* Here is my identification tag.

CAPTAIN VESEY

Notarize those papers proper up at the courthouse. Don't be too proud around white men, this still a slave state.

DENMARK VESEY

Maybe so, but I am a free man.

Market people of Charleston enter. Women carry baskets of fruit and vegetables on their heads, men mingle with the women selling their wares.

PETER POYAS

First thing he bought was a pair of shoes.

DENMARK VESEY

And I walked in my freedom shoes.

MARKET WOMAN

Shrimp Ra-Ra!

MARKET WOMAN

Gumbo Ya-Ya!

MARKET WOMAN

Come here for my chili peppers!

MARKET WOMAN

Sweet oranges!

MARKET WOMAN

Fresh coconut!

MARKET WOMAN

Carolina sweet peaches!

PETER POYAS

Up and down the city market... East Bay Street...Custom House Wharf...South Bay.

DENMARK VESEY

Morning to you!

CROWD

MORNIN' DENMARK!

DENMARK VESEY

You lookin' at a free man... Charleston!

MARKET WOMAN

Denmark Vesey, lemme see what a freedom paper look like.

DENMARK VESEY

Come over here and I'll be glad to show you.

Crowd gathers around Denmark.

PETER POYAS

They gathered around Denmark as moths to the light. Here stood one of our own. Holding in his mouth what most had never dared to swallow.

MARKET WOMAN

I tasted that freedom, just for a second. It was the seed of my unborn, walkin' us all into the 19th century.

GEORGE WILSON

(Entering with Bible) Church meeting tonight, brothers and sisters! In Jesus name, we will give thanks to the Lord.

CROWD

Amen!

DENMARK VESEY

George Wilson where you planning to have this church meeting?

GEORGE WILSON

My Master, who I serve on this earth, as I serve Jesus in heaven, has agreed to let us meet on the open ground near Balkley's Farm. Praise His Holy Name!

CROWD

Praise His Holy Name!

DENMARK VESEY

I want to be a class leader in your church.

GEORGE WILSON

Amen, brother. But you could join the Brown Fellowship Society. They only admit free men of color.

DENMARK VESEY

Free or enslaved aren't we all men standing here? *(Men shake their heads in agreement.)* Haven't these women born our children?

WOMEN

Amen!

DENMARK VESEY

I'll be my own free man.

GEORGE WILSON

Amen, brother.

CROWD

Amen.

PETER POYAS

Charleston had never seen a free man of color like Denmark.

CROWD

His freedom became our freedom,

PETER POYAS

Shaping the form of things to come.

Crowd begins to hum; "Go Down Moses" as Denmark comes center to preach the word.

DENMARK VESEY

"AND THE LORD SAID UNTO MOSES, RISE UP EARLY IN THE MORNING, AND STAND BEFORE PHARAOH, AND SAY UNTO HIM, THUS SAITH THE LORD GOD, LET MY PEOPLE GO."

CROWD

(Singing and Dancing) LET MY PEOPLE GO!

DENMARK VESEY

"FOR NOW I WILL STRETCH OUT MY HAND, THAT I MAY SMITE THEE AND THY PEOPLE WITH PESTILENCE; AND THOU SHALT BE CUT OFF FROM THE EARTH."

CROWD

(Singing and Dancing) LET MY PEOPLE GO!

DENMARK VESEY

"AND PHARAOH HARDENED HIS HEART AT THIS TIME ALSO, NEITHER WOULD HE LET THE PEOPLE GO."

Crowd stops as Beck approaches Denmark.

BECK

Time does not soften the heart of stone.

DENMARK VESEY

Patience, Beck.

BECK

He just let me go.

DENMARK VESEY

(Grabbing her) What you sayin'?

BECK

He sold me! Today, sold me to Masar Leveridge for two hundred and eighty-nine dollars.

DENMARK VESEY

Not so! I told him I give him five hundred for you!

BECK

What I been saying? All this time? He sleep with his evil closer than his own heart.

DENMARK VESEY

(Shouting) You my wife!

BECK

Maybe so, but you won't see me again.

DENMARK VESEY

What kind of freedom have I paid for?

BECK

You free to keep your wage at the end of the day.

DENMARK VESEY

But not free enough to put my wife in my bed!

BECK

I don't want you comin' up there to try and find me.

DENMARK VESEY

Where he taking you?

BECK

Out by Hampstead.

DENMARK VESEY

I'll be there Sunday.

BECK

No! We gonna end this thing right now. Children grown. I got nothing more of yours to carry. Let me walk outa here with my soul free. Give me that! I can't live no more 6 days for 1 hour on the Sabbath.

DENMARK VESEY

Let me try and talk to Leveridge.

BECK

That's what I am saying! You ain't listening to me! I can't cook your food. I can't wash your clothes. I can't lay down with you. You can't hold me but 1 hour on Sunday. I want you dead to me. I want to go up there to Hampstead and bury you proper. Give me that.

DENMARK VESEY

But I live for those Sundays.

BECK

It's not enough.

Beck leaves in sorrow, the crowd solemnly disassembles. Women leave playing area as men of the insurrection begin to consult on their situation.

PETER POYAS

Things began to change for Denmark after Beck left. He saw freedom as something belonging to all Americans. Got himself a house on Bull Street right in the heart of the city. We would sit up in there late into the night.

DENMARK VESEY

We hold these truths to be self evident…that all men are created equal.

MONDAY GELL

If you not quoting the Bible you quoting the Constitution. When you gonna get it? You a Black man in a White country.

DENMARK VESEY

I am a free man in a country called America. Nothing else gonna face His Maker on the day I die!

GULLAH JACK

(Running in with Batteau) Napolean has been destroyed in Haiti!

BATTEAU

    Fifty Thousand Africans have set fire to every French sugar cane on the island.

DENMARK VESEY

    Their leader?

GULLAH JACK

    Touissant L'Ouverture.

BATTEAU

    He was a slave just like us.

DENMARK VESEY

    Leading the people to revolution.

GULLAH JACK

    The first African power in the New World.

PETER POYAS

    We were all with Touissant that night.

    Distant drums come up as the spirit of revolution inspires the men.

GULLAH JACK

    American Revolution! French Revolution! Haitian Revolution!

MEN

    Revolution!

DENMARK VESEY

    Decide!*(Pointing to Batteau)* Do you stand here free or slave?

BATTEAU

    Free!

DENMARK VESEY:

    Gullah! What do you bend to hear?

GULLAH JACK

    I hear Mother Africa Rage!
    Wounded! The womb of the continent bleeds.
    Her entrails reach across the Atlantic.
    With Obatala they come crawling across the sea.
    I watch the crossing. One with the First Ancestor.
    Peace belongs to no man who will not fight the battle.
    OBATALA turn to OGUN! Warriors AWAKE! The gods stir!

DENMARK VESEY

    They say we can't fight the white man. But who is the white man? A farmer that put a rifle in one hand, Declaration of Independence in the other. We fought with them, side by side, to bring down the mighty British. Now I say, we can take them in Charleston.

MEN

    Preach the word.

DENMARK VESEY

We are God's chosen people in a godless land. We got to rise up against Pharoah!

MEN

RISE UP!

DENMARK VESEY

We got to preach as Jesus in Luke, 11:23 "He who is not with me is against me".

MONDAY GELL

What you think, you some kinda Moses?

DENMARK VESEY

George Washington, John Adams, Thomas Jefferson stood up for theirs.

GULLAH JACK

Now what you got to say?

MONDAY GELL

Any white man get a sniff of this we all be hung.

NED BENNETT

Ain't no white man gonna know a thing if we don't tell them.

ROLLA BENNETT

Remember that, Monday!

DENMARK VESEY

Once we've set sail for the Caribbean them that's left will know all about it.

MONDAY GELL

You mean for us to leave then?

DENMARK VESEY

I am going to lead this revolt up and down the coast and then exodus.

MONDAY GELL

And where's a bunch of revoltin' slaves gonna head to?

PETER POYAS

I want to walk on the land belonging to the first black nation in the New World.

GEORGE WILSON

(Entering) Brother Denmark.

DENMARK VESEY

Come in, Brother George.

GEORGE WILSON

Evening.

MEN

Evening.

GEORGE WILSON
This just take a minute.

DENMARK VESEY
Speak your mind, George Wilson.

GEORGE WILSON
Our church been closed.

NED BENNETT
What?

GEORGE WILSON
Guess we just been shouting and praising the name too loud.

PETER POYAS
Those devils closed down our church?

GEORGE WILSON
I will not listen to blasphemy. We got to pray harder that's all. I gots to go get Master's supper ready.

DENMARK VESEY
You lucky to have such a good Master, George Wilson.

GEORGE WILSON
Amen, brother.

DENMARK VESEY
You never once thought to disobey him?

GEORGE WILSON:
Never once! I swear before Jesus!

DENMARK VESEY
You best get back to cook his supper.

GEORGE WILSON
Just where I'm heading! *(Exits)*

PETER POYAS
Never trust a man who wears his Master's old coat!

DENMARK VESEY
It's time.

NED BENNETT
I'm with you.

ROLLA BENNETT
Count me in.

GULLAH JACK
This is our day.

PETER POYAS

Let's do it.

BATTEAU

No turning back.

MONDAY GELL

Alright.

DENMARK VESEY

This is the plan. (*Unveiling a map of Charleston*) The revolution will begin at midnight July 14, 1822. Peter. Lead your men from South Bay to Meeting Street. Capture the guardhouse across from St. Michael's Church. Send a hundred men inside to seize the arms and ammunition.

PETER POYAS

We will be ready!

DENMARK VESEY

Ned! Lead your men to seize the United States Arsenal on the Neck.

NED BENNETT

Where should I gather them?

DENMARK VESEY

Gadsen's Wharf.

NED BENNETT

We'll be there.

DENMARK VESEY

Rolla! Lead your group from Bennett Mills after you have killed the Governor.

ROLLA BENNETT

I understand what must be done.

DENMARK VESEY

Gullah! I'm countin' on you to bring in the Sea Island people.

GULLAH JACK

I have crab claws for all my men!

MONDAY GELL

Why you got to mess with conjure?

DENMARK VESEY

(*Ignoring Monday's comment*) Enter the city from the East and take the Duke's store.

GULLAH JACK

From now until the revolution, the Gullah will make ceremony.

MONDAY GELL

Ceremony? This fool is gonna get a rope around his neck with all his foolishness.

GULLAH JACK

Why you here if you do not believe in the power of Africa?

MONDAY GELL

I believe in Monday Gell!

ROLLA BENNETT

(To Monday) Are you with us or against us?

PETER POYAS

You better decide right now, Monday. Gullah Jack is one of us.

MONDAY GELL

Still don't like that little witch doctor.

GULLAH JACK

When a thousand of my Sea Island people enter the city, then you will remember the motherland.

DENMARK VESEY

Batteau, you will be my side when we take the Old Guardhouse. We will free every Black man in prison and head for the wharf.

MONDAY GELL

Where are we gonna get the ships?

DENMARK VESEY

Three ships will be docked ready to sail for the Caribbean. When Mingo gives you the signal lead your men straight for those ships at midnight. They will take us to Haiti.

MINGO

I'll be there to give you the signal, just have your men ready.

MONDAY GELL

Can we do this?

DENMARK VESEY

(Putting his hands on Monday's shoulders)
Monday, my brother, I don't know. But I am ready to die trying.

MEN

(Placing their hands together) He who is not with us is against us.

The men leave as George Wilson appears looking out over the bay. Monday Gell walks up to George.

MONDAY GELL

Afternoon, George.

GEORGE WILSON

Monday.

MONDAY GELL

Yeah, won't be long now.

GEORGE WILSON

Amen, brother.

MONDAY GELL

You don't even know what's about to take place. See that flag flying? That ship is about to take one thousandf brothers to freedom. Just as soon as we take this city.

GEORGE WILSON

What you say?

MONDAY GELL

Nothing. Forget what I said. I didn't mean anything by it.

GEORGE WILSON

Stay away from me!

George limps out hurriedly but is met by Peter Poyas, Mingo Harth, and Rolla Bennett.

GEORGE WILSON

You three in on this?

PETER POYAS

What you talking about, George?

GEORGE WILSON

Leave me be!

George Wilson rushes off to tell his master about the plan.

MINGO HARTH

What did you tell him?

MONDAY GELL

We was just passing time.

PETER POYAS

Rolla! Get over to Denmark! Tell him George Wilson knows.

ROLLA BENNETT

(To Monday) I should slit your throat! *(Rolla runs out)*

MONDAY GELL

He can't prove nothing.

PETER POYAS

I'm gonna head up to the country. *(Peter and Mingo run out)*
Shut up! Mingo…head over to the Islands, let Gullah know.

MONDAY GELL

What about me?

(He runs out as Market women run in)

MARKET WOMAN

They've taken Peter Poyas to the Workhouse!

MARKET WOMAN

Governor put Rolla and Ned in the prison!

MARKET WOMAN

Gullah Jack has been brought in from the Sea Islands!

MARKET WOMAN

They've chained Batteau and Mingo Harth!

MARKET WOMAN

Denmark Vesey has been captured!

Denmark and Peter enter in chains.

DENMARK VESEY

They don't have anything on us. We have shed no blood.

PETER POYAS

As long as we do not turn on each other we will walk out of here as men.

The men of the insurrection enter in chains and turn their backs as Monday Gell comes forward.

MONDAY GELL

(*Shaking*) Don't turn your back like I'm some Judas! I ain't gonna hang for some crazy mess of Denmark Vesey! That's right. Denmark Vesey thought up the whole stinkin' plan. All this foolishness about slaves being free men. I knew somethin' bad was gonna come of it! Brought in that Sea Island Gullah to work conjure. Ned and Rolla 'cause Governor Bennett trusted them. I heard him tell Rolla to go kill the Governor. Just as calm as you sittin' there. Batteau, why he think Denmark some kinda Moses. Peter Poyas he never trust anyone that do right by his Master. He just as guilty. Denmark Vesey read us the Bible, then the Constitution. Say America belong to all of us. I never did believe in the insurrection.

Judge attired in long black robe and white wig comes forward.

JUDGE HAMILTON

Peter Poyas, how do you plead?

PETER POYAS

A man is innocent until proven guilty. I am not guilty, Judge Hamilton.

JUDGE HAMILTON

Ned Bennett how do you plead?

NED BENNETT

Not guilty!

JUDGE HAMILTON

Rolla Bennett how do you plead?

ROLLA BENNETT

I been with the Governor fifteen years! I am innocent!

JUDGE HAMILTON

Jack Pritchard, how do you plead?

GULLAH JACK

Gullah Jack has done nothing to be here!

JUDGE HAMILTON

Batteau Bennett, how do you plead?

BATTEAU

Not guilty!

JUDGE HAMILTON

Mingo Harth, how do you plead?

MINGO HARTH

I plead for my life Judge. I am a working man! An innocent man!

JUDGE HAMILTON

Denmark Vesey, how do you plead?

DENMARK VESEY

Would you hang me for my thoughts? This court spits on the face of justice! We have shed no blood in this city! What man or woman you hold in chains has not prayed for freedom? This country is founded on the ideals set forth in the Declaration of Independence, which state that all men are created equal. And as men are we not granted the right to think…to speak our minds! If you hang us, you hang us for our thoughts! These are innocent men standing before you Judge Hamilton!

JUDGE HAMILTON

Denmark Vesey, how do you plead?

DENMARK VESEY

I am not guilty.

JUDGE HAMILTON

Monday Gell, you alone amongst your compatriots have proven to be a loyal citizen of Charleston. The Court finds you innocent you are free to go. *(Monday Gell leaves the Courtroom)* Denmark Vesey, Ned Bennett, Rolla Bennet, Jack Pritchard, Mingo Harth, Batteau Bennett, Peter Poyas. The court, after considering all the circumstances, finds you guilty of planning an insurrection against the city and people of Charleston. You will remain in solitary confinement until the morning of July second, five days from this sentence, at which time you will be hung from the neck until dead. COURT DISMISSED.

The sound of a sorrow song comes up, as women enter, convicted men walk up platform. A guard puts a rope around the neck of each man.

JUDGE HAMILTON

Your days on earth are now at a close. You stand upon the confines of eternity. While you linger on this side of the grave, what be your last word?

MEN
FREEDOM!

Men raise their hands in victory. Immediate darkness. Soulful music comes up, slowly lights raise, men have left the playing area and a praise dance of spiritual upliftment is performed by women in white. As dance concludes the raging of African drums fills the playing area.

FADE TO BLACK

End of Play

ASANTE
Princess of Harlem
by Carolyn Nur Wistrand

CHARACTERS

Joey - Bartender at Eddie Diamond's Club

Eddie Diamond - Owner of the club

Lavender Lacy - Eddie Diamond's Showgirl

Showgirls at Club - Pretty Prissy Linda Lime Vanilla Velma Butterscotch Brenda, Nelly Bly

The Cinder Family - Ella Cinder Carrie Cinder Liza Cinder Mrs. Cinder

Johnny Jett - The Harlem Spelling Man

JoJo Ned - The Detroit Spelling Man

Nasty Boy - JoJo Ned's Back Up

Trish the Dish - JoJo Ned's Woman

One Eyed Louie - Eddie Diamond's Number One Thug

Connie Coconut - One Eyed Louie's Girl

Mama Lola - Harlem Fortune Teller

Speller Driller - Spelling Card Gangster

Royal Ghanaian Ancestral Court - Asantihene Asantemena Royal Spirits African Drummers

EDDIE DIAMOND'S CLUB
Harlem
1934

Club is dark, chairs stacked on top of tables. Appropriate 1930's music fills the club as Joey strolls in. Lights softly come up as he begins to set chairs down. He grabs a towel from the bar, and speaks to the audience as he works.

JOEY

Heah! How you'all doin? You see how my nights goin! Diamond don't pay half what I'm worth. Since them stocks fell in '29….times are bad up here! Back in the 20's, all the high steppers from downtown used to be in here. Now days, half the city looking for a nickel.

Old Beggar walks in with a bowl.

BEGGAR

Mistah! Could you spare a little broth?

JOEY

Can't you read the sign? We closed!

BEGGAR

Please, Mistah!

JOEY

This is Diamond's Club not the Soup Kitchen.

BEGGAR

Spare a piece of bread, son.

JOEY

Get on outa here with all that. Half a Harlem hungry!

Taking the broom he shoves her out as Ella Cinder walks in.

JOEY

Where you been, Ella?

ELLA

Mrs. Johnson's babies was in there all alone, Joey. I'm still an hour early.

JOEY

You want bread scraps for them brats?

ELLA

You know I do!

JOEY

I told you two hours early! Get that back door polished before Diamond gets in here. *(Exits)*

Ella takes a large bucket from behind the bar and crosses to the door.

The Beggar reappears.

BEGGAR

Could you spare some broth, Miss?

ELLA

Are you that hungry?

BEGGAR

Honey, I haven't touched food in four days!

ELLA

I don't have much…but here…take this bread.

JOEY

(*Yelling from cellar*) Get down here and clean out the mops. Ella Cinder!

ELLA

Wish I had more to give you.

BEGGAR

Someone gone bless you for this.

Beggar exits into the cold street as Ella runs downstairs. Pretty Prissy, Nelly Bly, Butterscotch Brenda, Linda Lime, and Vanilla Velma enter.

PRISSY

What's this? Ella doesn't have our supper set!

NELLY

Where is that little rag muffin?

Joey enters with a case of bottles.

VELMA

Hey, Joey! Like my new dress.

JOEY

(*Ignoring her*) Sure, kid.

PRISSY

(*Circles center*) What about mine?

JOEY

(*Continuing to work*) Sweet. Real sweet.

PRISSY

(*Stomping her feet*) You ain't even looked.

SHOWGIRLS

What's wrong with you?

JOEY

Just trying to get ready for the night, girls.

SHOWGIRLS

Where's Ella with our supper?

JOEY

Downstairs…she only got two hands.

PRISSY

She better start using them.

SHOWGIRLS

We hungry!

Joey stops in his tracks as a cold spirit fills the room.

JOEY

Bad nights a comin'!

SHOWGIRLS

What you talkin'?

JOEY

Cold wind just come down my back!

Girls back away from Joey.

VELMA

This ain't the spook house!

JOEY

Bad nights a comin'! Feel it in my bones!

PRISSY

I don't want to hear your ole timey superstition. Get Ella Cinder up here with my supper.

JOEY

Bad nights a comin'!

Eddie Diamond strolls in with Lavender Lacey. Jake follows them in.

EDDIE

Glass a milk, Joey, one up. What do you have, Lacey?

LACEY

Same as you, Eddie.

EDDIE

Two glasses of milk, straight up!

PRISSY

No wonder you so strong, Eddie Diamond, drinkin' all that milk.

EDDIE

Yeah…My Daddy was a bootlegger. Shipped whisky from Virginia to Tennessee, but he never touched the stuff. Said, "Son, a real man drinks his milk".

SHOWGIRLS

Oh, Eddie! How you can talk!

EDDIE

Stick with me, Lacey, you'll always have something to listen to!

LACEY

Where else would I want to be?

Ella enters with two buckets, mops, brushes, and begins to clean the floor.

PRISSY

I wouldn't mind listening to something, Eddie Diamond.

EDDIE

You wearing that red dress, Prissy.

LACEY

Eddie!

VELMA

Careful, Prissy.

Joey brings the jug of milk and two glasses.

PRISSY

I said I wouldn't mind listenin' to something.

LACEY

Go get the piano player to play you a song.

EDDIE

Here, Lacey, drink up.

LACEY

I will, as soon as she shuts up!

PRISSY

You about to spill milk all over your lavender dress.

EDDIE

Now Lacey, Prissy didn't mean anything. After all, the girls want to listen to what I got to say.

SHOWGIRLS

Oh, Eddie! How you can talk!

PRISSY

But, Eddie, Ella ain't cooked our supper.

EDDIE

What?

ELLA

Stew's cooking right now, Mr. Diamond.

EDDIE

That stew shoulda been ready an hour ago…what you been doing?

ELLA

There hasn't been heat in the tenements for a week. Miss Johnson's youngest baby coughing so bad got influenza. Hospital say no free medicine till Friday…it being Friday she took the baby and the other babies in there alone.

EDDIE

You was told to be in here two hours early if you wanted a job.

JOEY

I told her, boss…she showed up an hour late!

ELLA

I couldn't let that baby die, Mr. Diamond.

EDDIE

You want a job as a nurse, go to the hospital. You girls got a number to get ready for.

PRISSIE

But, Eddie! The dressing rooms aren't clean!

EDDIE

What?

NELLY

There's clothes on the floor!

LINDA

Nylons on the table!

VELMA

Pins on the chairs!

SHOWGIRLS

The place is filthy!

NELLY

And that lazy Ella Cinder is an hour late!

PRISSY

And her lazy sisters ain't shown their faces!

JOEY

Bad nights comin'! Feel it in my bones!

EDDIE

ELLA!

ELLA

They gone be here, Mr. Diamond.

EDDIE

They better be here! Tell you what, gals, couldn't ya just clean the place for Eddie Diamond one time?

PRISSY
But my clothes!

BRENDA
My lips!

LINDA
My fingernails!

VELMA
My hair!

SHOWGIRLS
We ain't the maids!

LACEY
Coulda fooled me.

JOEY
Bad nights a comin'.

SHOWGIRLS
Stuff it Joey!

Showgirls stomp off to their dressing room as One Eyed Louie walks in with Connie Coconut.

LOUIE
I fixed it, boss.

CONNIE
Yeah, you shoulda seen Louie.

EDDIE
How much you get?

Louie smoothly lays down a fifty, twenty, and ten, one at a time.

LOUIE
Fifty from Old Man Sanders. Twenty from Blind boy Blue. Ten from Old Lady Hernandez.

Eddie jumps up and hits the table.

EDDIE
Hernandez owes me three months rent!

CONNIE
Mr. Diamond…she got twelve kids in there!

EDDIE
And they livin' in one of my tenements! Go collect the rest.

LOUIE
And if she won't pay?

EDDIE
Throw 'em in the street!

LOUIE

It's covered, boss.

CONNIE

C'mon, Eddie, that lady must be ninety years old if she's a day.

EDDIE

Don't tell me any sob story. Listen, how do you think I became Eddie Diamond? By givin' handouts to every bum that walks the streets? I seen them aching bellies up and down Harlem too many times. In my line, you gotta be tough! Pour me another milk.

JOEY

Yes sir, Mr. Diamond.

Carrie, Liza, and Mrs. Cinder walk in.

LOUIE

Here come the rest of your scrub women, Boss.

CONNIE

Poor Ella, her mama look like she just stepped out of the sewer.

Lacey takes her perfume out and spraying herself, walks up to the bar.

LACEY

Look at her two sisters! Can't you get any decent help, Eddie?

LOUIE

Have the rats been eating your clothes?

CARRIE

Well Mr. Louie, I woke up in the middle of the night and there was a big rat on my bed.

EDDIE

There's no rats in my tenements.

CARRIE

Well, Mr. Diamond, it was this big. I never saw a mouse that big.

Eddie throws the mop out of Carrie's hand.

EDDIE

I just said I don't have rats in my tenements.

ELLA

My sister don't lie, Mr. Diamond.

EDDIE

(Clenching his fists) Ohhhhhhh!

Eddie walks over threateningly and stands in front of the Cinder girls, who are shaking.

CONNIE

You got the Boss mad!

EDDIE

No, I'm gonna pretend I didn't hear that. Get back to work!

Liza accidentally bumps into Louie. He shoves her to the floor.

LOUIE

Watch where you're sweepin'!

EDDIE

You two hurry up with that floor, the girls dressing rooms are dirty! What are you hanging around here for?

MRS CINDER

I need a word with you, Mr. Diamond.

EDDIE

I'll give you a word. Cash. The green kind!

MRS CINDER

Mr. Diamond, I need time! You got my three girls workin' 'til their fingers bleed.

EDDIE

When your ole man died....did I throw you in the streets?

Eddie crosses back to his table and takes out a cigar, Lacey lights the cigar.

MRS. CINDER

No, Mr. Diamond.

EDDIE

When you come to me and say, my three girls need work. Did I give them jobs?

MRS. CINDER

Yes, Mr. Diamond.

EDDIE

You got three girls working and you can't make rent?

MRS. CINDER

That's what I'm trying to get to. You only paying them five dollars a month and you charging us thirty dollars a month rent.

EDDIE

Each one of them making five dollars a month...that's fifteen dollars.

MRS. CINDER

Yes sir, Mr. Diamond. But, fifteen dollars for three girls working fourteen hours a day, seven days a week, that still leaves us fifteen dollars a month we come up short, and no money for food.

EDDIE

Food? I give those girls scraps from my table.

MRS. CINDER

I mean a hot meal. A little beef...fresh fruit.

EDDIE

A hot meal? You want them girls to get a hot meal? Ain't that sweet boys?

JOEY/LOUI/JAKE

Touches my heart.

MRS. CINDER

Liza ain't said a word since my husband passed last winter.

EDDIE

She don't need to talk to scrub my floor!

MRS. CINDER

I been takin' in wash, scrubbin' eight tenements a week, to get you that extra money, but we so hungry, Mr. Diamond.

EDDIE

Half of this country hungry. We in a Depression. And you is wasting my time.

MRS. CINDER

I'm going, Mr. Diamond, but I gotta ask you, I prayed and..

EDDIE

Get to it!

MRS. CINDER

Could you please give Ella a raise? She been comin' in here two hours early for the past five months. Please sir, think about it.

EDDIE

You hear that, boys? The ole lady wants to know if her dust mop daughter could get a raise. You hear that, boys?

JOEY/LOUI/JAKE

Yeah, we heard that.

EDDIE

Well, give her a raise.

Joey, Jake, and Louie sinisterly move over to Ella, pick her up off the floor, and hold her in mid-air.

MRS. CINDER

Please! Put her down!

They throw her on the floor.

EDDIE

She got her raise.

MRS. CINDER

What are you trying to do, break her legs?

EDDIE

I'm letting you know, your time is finished. You go get me that fifteen dollars! I don't care if you have to scrub every street in Harlem. GET MY MONEY.

MRS. CINDER

Yes, Mr. Diamond.

EDDIE

Dump her in the street!

Joey grabs Mrs. Cinder and pushes her out.

JOEY

This way, Mrs. Cinder.

JoJo Ned, Trish, and Nasty Boy walk into the club.

JOJO NED

Where's Jett?

EDDIE

Johnny Jett?

JOJO NED

That's right.

EDDIE

Hard to say. Who's asking?

JOJO NED

Jo Jo Ned is asking.

EDDIE

You boys ever heard of JoJo Ned?

JOEY/LOUI/JAKE

Never heard of him.

TRISH

Well you lookin' at him!

EDDIE

Lady, I'm just stating facts.

JOJO NED

Well get this fact straight.
(Rhyme/Rap)
IM JO JO NED CLEVER IN THE HEAD
WINNIN SPELLIN BEES SINCE THE AGE OF THREE
READIN ALL THEM WORDS IN
WEBSTERS DICTIONARY
I DON'T LIKE TO LOSE
SO YOU BETTER CHOOSE
JOHNNY JETT OR ME
WHAT ITS GONNA BE?

EDDIE

We'll have to wait and see.

JOJO/TRISH

What?

EDDIE

Game don't start 'til ten. Come back then.

JOJO NED

Ten? We'll be back.

TRISH

(*Snapping her fingers*) Yeah, the place is starting to smell.

JOEY

Bad nights a comin'! Feel it in my bones.

As they begin to walk out a flurry of activity commences.

EDDIE

Ella! Bring me another milk straight up!

LOUIE

Carrie! Bring me a peppermint twist!

CONNIE

Liza! Bring me an orange spritz!

Showgirls stomp in angrily and throw the Cinder girls around.

PRISSY

Iron my dress!

NELLY

Find my brush!

BRENDA

Get my stockings!

VELMA

Where's our supper?!

EDDIE

Get that floor swept now!

The Asante Ancestors enter and raising their staffs, the crowd is stilled.

ASANTEMENA

So this is Harlem.

ASANTIHENE

A long way from Ghana.

ASANTEMENA

A long way from the golden stool of Asante.

ASANTIHENE

We must find her!

ASANETMENA
  The lost Ghanaian of our tribe!

ASANTIHENE
  But they are empty of spirit.

ASHANTEMENA
  The scent of the Queen breathes.

ASANTIHENE
  Perhaps it is the cheap perfume of this city.

ASHANTEMENA
  I tell you she is near! Bend low.

ASANTIHENE:
  The three on the floor? They are servants.

ASANTEMENA
  When the Ocean Mother wept
  She stood on Coral and Pearl
  Elmina Castle of Cape Coast
  Held the Lost Daughters of Asante
  Buried in the Harlem Mecca
  The Scent of Jasmine Breathes.

ASANTIHENA
  They are servant girls.

ASANTEMENA
  The Spirits Do Not Lie! Tell me Asantihena.

ASANTIHENA
  (She bends low and smells the sweetness of the jasmine)
  The Spirits Do Not Lie!

ASANTIHENA/ASANTEMENA
  Asante!

ASANTEMENA
  We must prepare for the ceremony.

  The African Spirits raise their staffs and leave. The club returns to frenzied activity.

EDDIE
  (To Carrie and Liza) You two, downstairs. Girls, get ready. Ella, finish up here.

  Showgirls move towards dressing room as Johnny Jett enters.

SHOWGIRLS
  Heah, Johnny.

JOHNNY
  Jo Jo Ned show up yet?

EDDIE

That Detroit Thug?

JOHNNY

He been in here?

EDDIE

Might have.

JOHNNY

Tonights the count.

Joey pours Johnny his regular drink.

JOEY

How much did you take him for last night?

JOHNNY

Nearly three hundred.

Joey puts the juice down as Jett takes a bill out to pay him.

EDDIE

I don't want no trouble in here tonight, Jett.

JOHNNY

Look, Diamond, my business been supporting this place for years. A little trouble…keeps the place jumpin'.

JOEY

Bad nights a comin'.

EDDIE

Louie, you keep an eye on the back door tonight. Anything happens…call the tip off before the coppers show.

LOUIE

It's covered, Boss.

EDDIE

C'mon, Lacey, get some of that stew, before it get cold.

LACEY

I thought you was taking me out to supper.

EDDIE

Later baby, you need to eat and get ready for the show.

Eddie and Lacey go downstairs.

JOHNNY

How's your Mama, Ella?

ELLA

Not as good as she could be, Mr. Jett.

JOHNNY
Word has it, Diamond's sky-rocketin' the rent.

ELLA
Times are hard, Mr. Jett.

JOHNNY
My name is Johnny.

ELLA
I know that.

JOHNNY
Even in those rags, you the prettiest girl in Harlem, Ella Cinder.

ELLA
I don't know about all that, Mr. Jett.

JOHNNY
You don't need to know. One of these days, you and me all the way.

ELLA
You got a woman, Mr. Jett.

JOHNNY
Yeah, but you got my heart.

ELLA
I got to get back to work. Help my Mama make rent.

JOHNNY
(Hands her a bill) Here, take this home to your Mama.

NELLY
(Slinking in) Take what home to her Mama?

JOHNNY
Keep that, baby.

NELLY
What he hand you?

ELLA
Just something for my Mama.

NELLY
Something for your Mama?

JOHNNY
Lay off, Nelly.

NELLY
Johnny is my man!

ELLA

Why everybody knows that, Nelly Bly.

NELLY

Everybody but you it seems. Look rag muffin, I'm giving you fair warning. I don't ever want to see you dragging your sorry self in front of Johnny again!

ELLA

I..I…

NELLY

You got that?

ELLA

Ah…

NELLY

Now go scrub out my dressing room, you left some dirt in the back corner last night.

Eddie reappears.

EDDIE

Move, Ella. You done with your sweepin' up here.

NELLY

Make sure you clean my dressing room first….after all, I am the star around here.

Ella crosses to the downstairs as Nelly slinks towards Johnny.

JOHNNY

Don't come over here with all that.

NELLY

With all what, baby?

JOHNNY

I told you to quit messing with that girl.

EDDIE

(Crossing back to his table.) You better watch your man, Nelly.

JOHNNY

Keep out of this, Diamond.

NELLY

What's wrong, honey?

JOHNNY

Got a lot on my mind. Tonight's the big game. Stakes are high.

NELLY

What's your plan?

JOHNNY

Take him out by the third game.

NELLY
And if you don't?

JOHNNY
Play the tricksters fate.

NELLY
Either way…you're the winner.

Pretty Prissy angrily enters from dressing room stairs and crosses to Eddie.

PRISSY
Eddie, you need to hire someone who can scrub these floors. My dressing room is filthy.

EDDIE
You sure wearing that dress.

PRISSY
You like it that much?

EDDIE
Red's my favorite color.

PRISSY
That's what I heard.

EDDIE
Who told you that?

PRISSY
I got my ways.

EDDIE
I can see that.

PRISSY
What else you see?

EDDIE
You on my arm, going over to Jake's for a big steak. What you say?

PRISSY
You the boss, Mr. Diamond.

EDDIE
Let's do this!

PRISSY
Alright.

EDDIE
Don't start the game till I get back, Jett.

JOHNNY
I start the game when JoJo Ned shows up.

EDDIE

Easy, Jett.

JOHNNY

Go eat your steak dinner…Diamond.

EDDIE

I intend to do just that. C'mon, Pretty…I need some air.

Eddie and Prissy stroll out arm in arm.

CONNIE

That two timin' creep! Wait 'til Lacey finds out!

LOUIE

(Grabbing her arm) And just how is that goin' to happen?

CONNIE

I'm going to tell her!

LOUIE

You're going to keep your mouth shut!

CONNIE

You're hurting me!

LOUIE

You don't mess with my boss!

JOHNNY

Knock it off, Louie.

LOUIE

You ain't gonna say nothing to Lacey!

JOHNNY

I said knock it off!

LOUIE

Stay out of this, Jett!

JOHNNY

Long as you hurting that girl I'm in it!

LOUIE

My job is to watch Diamond's back.

JOHNNY

As his gopher? Hurting women? You don't have the brains to get a real job.

LOUIE

(Releasing Connie and crossing to Jett) You call dealing cards a real job? How many brains does that take?

JOHNNY

Quite a few! You gots to be fast in the head to call the shots. You gots to read! Spell them words…FAST!! Not just blow off a bunch of air.

CONNIE

You a prince…Johnny Jett.

NELLY

Sure are….Prince of Blues Alley.

LOUIE

You dames are all alike. Don't know a real man when you see one.

CONNIE

A real man? I'm sure not looking at one!

Connie stomps out the backdoor.

LOUIE

Don't you walk out on me! Connie! (*Running after her*) Wait up, woman! I didn't mean it!

JOEY

Bad nights a comin'. Feel it in my bones.

Mama Lola, the fortune teller of Harlem enters dressed in native Caribbean attire. She carries a velvet red bag filled with bones and oils and speaks in a thick French patois of the French West Indies.

MAMA LOLA

Ze night is special, Joey! Ze stars comin out for Johnny tonight!

JOEY

Mama Lola! What you be seeing in your snake bag?

MAMA LOLA

I see zee moon! Dancing with a lost princess!

JOHNNY

I been looking for you up and down Harlem, Mama Lola.

MAMA LOLA

For this reason I come!

NELLY

What you need with that old lady's bag of tricks?

MAMA LOLA

You looking for trouble, girl? No problem, Mama Lola got something for you!

NELLY

I didn't mean nothing by it.

MAMA LOLA

Mama Lola don't play zat!!

JOHNNY

Get on girl, get on.

NELLY

But Johnny…

JOHNNY

I told you, tonights the big game, I need Mama Lola's charm.

NELLY

Alright, baby.

Nelly leaves to Johnny's relief. Nelly stares back at Johnny, but he does not give her a second glance.

MAMA LOLA

Zhu have to pay double…zhu need my conjure tonight.

Johnny throws down a twenty dollar bill.

MAMA LOLA

Double!

Johnny throws down another twenty.

JOHNNY

Ah pays ya! Double! Tell me what I needs to know.

Mama Lola ceremoniously takes out her glass ball and puts it on the table.

MAMA LOLA

This is the night! The Ancient Night! The Mystery Night!

JOHNNY

Word on the street…JoJo Ned bringing in back up.

MAMA LOLA

Zee only back up for JoJo Ned is in his head!

JOHNNY

What round do I take him out in?

MAMA LOLA

(*Breathing heavily*) Zee power of tonight is not in cards!

JOHNNY

What you say? JoJo Ned gonna take me the first round?

MAMA LOLA

No! Tonight something else will happen.

JOHNNY

Get the ball on the cards, mama! I gots to win this game!

MAMA LOLA

Something coming stronger! I lay down zee bones!

JOHNNY

Ah needs to know what hand to take him out on!

Mama Lola rummages through her bag and finds cat bones. She shakes the bones ceremoniously as all three chant.

MAMA LOLA

Cat bone, fish bone, gumbo stew, power of the hoodoo come on through! *(Throws down bones.)*

JOEY

(Hiding under a table) Those bones moving!

JOHNNY

Moving? What hand do I take him out on?

MAMA LOLA

Zee bones don't move to poker! Zee bones are moving with zee moon!

JOEY

What they saying, Mama Lola?

MAMA LOLA

Zee speak of love!

JOHNNY

What you mean...love?

JOEY

Johnny don't need no more love! He gots Nelly Bly!

MAMA LOLA

Zee bones do not move to hoochie coochie!

JOHNNY

What then?

MAMA LOLA

True love, Johnny.

JOEY

Look at them bones! They just made a heart.

MAMA LOLA

Zis is your heart, Johnny. Your heart has seen gold dust in the spirit of a woman.

JOHNNY

Pack up them cat bones! Bring out them snakes! Gimme the score on tonights high rolling stakes!

MAMA LOLA

Zee Mambo move in danger. Your sweet love face danger tonight !

JOEY

Bad nights a comin!

JOHNNY

Ah don't wanna hear this Mumbo Jumbo! I paid you double! What about the card game?

MAMA LOLA

Forget zee card game.

JOHNNY

You was paid to read them cards! Now you read them before I dump your cat bones in the sewer!

MAMA LOLA

Take him out on the third round.

JOHNNY

Third Round! That's it? *(Rising)*

MAMA LOLA

What about your true love, Johnny?

JOHNNY

Only thing on my mind is the game.

MAMA LOLA

Remember my words
Remember my power
There will be danger for love
At the midnight hour!

JOEY

Danger for love?

JOHNNY

I'm just a Harlem Spelling man,
Need a little magic
For the upper hand.
Women and Cards, Mama Lola...
just don't mix.
Mind gots to be strong
To use your tricks!

Johnny walks out.

MAMA LOLA

Stupid, stupid man!

JOEY

Pack up your bag, Mama Lola. This fortune telling session is through.

MAMA LOLA:

Do not speak to me! *(She throws her hand up in the air; Joey cringes)*

JOEY

Take your time, Mama Lola, take all the time you need.

Mama Lola walks out. Three Cinder girls return, carrying buckets.

ELLA

Dressing rooms clean, Joey.

JOEY

Then get them tables scrubbed down.

CARRIE

Can we have 5 minutes? Please, Joey?

JOEY

I said get them tables scrubbed!

Mrs. Cinder walks into the club.

ELLA

Mama!

CARRIE

Get on out of here, Mama!

JOEY

You was told not to come around here 'til you had the boss' money!

MRS. CINDER

Thats why I came back!

CARRIE

Mama! Please go home!

MRS. CINDER

I come to tell all three of you all. We can pay the rent!

ELLA

What you trying to say, Mama?

MRS. CINDER

Why it was some kinda magic. I was walkin' home and these spirits just come outa nowhere. They looked just like African Queens.

ELLA/CARRIE

African Queens?

MRS. CINDER

It was just a feeling that came over me. Like they were from Africa!

JOEY

They ain't got time to hear all this! Them tables dirty!

MRS. CINDER

You got time to git this gold to Boss Man!

JOEY

Gold?

ELLA

Where you get that gold, Mama?

MRS. CINDER

I'm tryin' to tell ya! I was walking home, prayin' hard, Lawd, I was prayin' hard and this vision come over me.

Asantemena and Asantihene enter and walk up to Mrs. Cinder as she remembers the meeting. Everyone else is momentarily suspended in the memory.

ASANTEMENA

Beloved Mother!

MRS. CINDER

You talking to me?

ASANTEMENA

The journey has not destroyed you, Mother.

MRS. CINDER

Who that talking?

ASANTEMENA

The hands of an Asante.

MRS. CINDER

Now somebody here be talking!

ASANTEMENA

The King that has given the Asante Queen a bed of roaches...this King shall himself taste the leopard's blood!

ASANTIHENA

You shall never be hungry...from this day forth.

ASANTEMENA

Go! Pay this King of the Slums.

Asantemena places gold in her hands. The African Spirits bow before Mrs. Cinder and floatingly depart.

MRS. CINDER

Then they was gone. I was standing there with pure gold in my hands.

JOEY

How you know that real gold?

MRS. CINDER

I know how gold feel to the touch. Come natural to me.

JOEY

Hand it all over. We'll see what the Boss say.

MRS. CINDER

You ain't taking all my gold. Here what I owe Mr. Diamond.

ELLA

Look here, Mama, Mr. Jett gave me another hundred.

MRS. CINDER

Mr. Jett? Girl, don't you be taking no money from these gangsters!

ELLA

He's a good man, Mama.

MRS. CINDER

A good man gots a good job. And I don't mean cards.

CARRIE

But, Mama, he give her the money to help you make rent.

MRS. CINDER

I got real gold in my pocket. I don't want that gambler's money! You understand me?

ELLA/CARRIE

Yes, Mama.

MRS. CINDER

Ah knew something was coming down tonight.

JOEY

Alright you paid out, now go on! Them tables ain't never gone shine with all this commotion. Get out!

MRS. CINDER

Get home before midnight girls. Magic never last too long.

ELLA/CARRIE

Yes, Mama.

JOEY

Now get this place clean!

ELLA

Joey, should I take their order?

JOEY

Whose order?

CARRIE

Those two.

JOEY

What two?

ELLA

Those two.

JOEY

Ain't nobody in here!

The African Ancestors raise their Staffs and halt Joey who becomes motionless in his tracks throughout their presence.

ASANTEMENA

From the other side of the Atlantic Ocean,

ASANTEHENE

Where the talking drums speak,

ASANTEMENA

On the white sands of West Africa,

ASANTEHENA

Your Asante Ancestors now greet! *(Spirits bow)*

ELLA

From where?

ASANTEMENA

The land below the blue coast. It is time to journey.

ASANTIHENA

Where dreams become the living flesh, of a day filled with dignity.

ELLA

Carrie, are you in my dream?

CARRIE

Are we in a dream?

ELLA

I don't know what's going on. Joey!

ANCESTORS

He cannot hear you.

ELLA

Liza, do you see Spirits?

Liza shakes her head yes.

CARRIE

African spirits.

Liza shakes her head yes.

ELLA

What do you want with us?

ASANTEMENA

We have come to lead you back.

ASANTIHENA

To the ancient memory.

ASANTEMENA

Of your royal ancestors.

ELLA

We ain't got no royal ancestors!

ASANTEMENA

Then you do not have spirit in your soul.

ELLA

Maybe we don't but we have corns on our toes!

CARRIE

Bumps on our hands!

ELLA/CARRIE

And work to do!

ASANTEMENA

Asante Princess! Never again will you scrub the Slum King's floor!

ASANTIHENA

Royal sisters! Never again will you wash the Slum King's tables!

ELLA

You give my Mama that gold?

ASANTEMENA

The gold of the Asante lies between heaven and earth.

ELLA

Maybe it's cause we so tired.

CARRIE

That's it Ella, we dreaming on our feet.

ASANTEMENA

Two hundred years we have waited for a pure drop of our Queen's blood.

CARRIE

This is Harlem! My sister ain't no Asante Princess! And you ain't no African Ancestors.

ELLA

A princess in Harlem? Only in a fairy tale!

ASANTEMENA

Ghana has a tale!

ASANTIHENA

A tale of great loss.

Drums begin to call the Ancestral Spirits to the playing area.

THE ANCIENT CEREMONY

The Cinder girls now become the Asante Princesses. African Drummers, African maidens carrying bowls of fruits on their heads, African elders, and the Queen Mother enter.

ASANTEMENA

Two hundred years ago the Asante prepared for the new Queen.

The Cinder girls are placed in the center of the ceremony, kneeling. The Queen Mother stands above the girls.

ASANTIHENA

Our queen was wise, beautiful and kind.

ASANTEMENA

Her sisters, the royal princesses, ruled by her side. The Beloved Mother guarded them. On the day of the ancient ceremony, three young girls were cleansed in sacred pools. The spirits of our ancestors entered the beloved daughters.

ASANTIHENA

No longer were they young girls, but three African queens.

Drumming. Cinder girls and Ancestors begin to dance as the drums rise in intensity.

ASANTEMENA

We stood by the sacred pools and saw the sacred vision given to Asante myth.

ELLA

Our great grandmother? A Queen?

ASANTIHENA

A Queen of much power!

ASANTEMENA

A Queen who held ancient secrets in her spirit! Her stolen history returns with you.

The girls now stare at the Ancient Queen who resembles their mother.

CINDER GIRLS

Mama!

ANCESTORS

Ancient Asante Queen!

Ancestors bow before the Queen.

ASANTEMENA

Asante Princess!

Ancestors bow before Ella Cinder.

ASANTIHENA

Royal Sisters of Asante!

Spirits bow before Carrie and Liza.

ELLA

Can this be true?

ASANTEMENA

If there ever was a true tale of Cinder Ella…it is you, Royal Ghanaians.

ANCESTORS

We must now prepare for the ceremony.

ELLA

Where are you taking us?

ASANTEMENA

To your homeland. Tonight the spirit world shall remember the Asante Princess.

CARRIE

Who's gonna finish up the work?

ASANTIHENA

Joey has two hands!

ANCESTORS

Tables dirty, boy! Clean 'em!

Joey comes back to life and scrubs at manic pace.

THE HARLEM SPELLING GAME

Music comes up. Harlem jazz of 1930'S.

Eddie Diamond, Johnny Jett, One-Eyed Loui, Jake, Speller Driller, and other gangsters enter club and take their seats.

Showgirls enter with sequined fans and perform a dance number.
As music fades, JoJo Ned walks in with Trish.

NELLY

Johnny! It's JoJo Ned! He's brought some back up.

NASTY BOY

So it's back to this dump.

EDDIE

Heah! Watch it!

NASTY BOY

I'm watching all right! Every one of you.

JOJO NED

There won't be any cheating tonight!

JOHNNY

Who you calling a cheater?

JOJO NED

The one I'm looking at!

EDDIE

Easy! I run a clean place. Theres no cheating at Eddie Diamond's. What do you have?

JOJO/NASTY

Lemon water.

JOJO NED

And the same for my woman.

TRISH

Get the game started, JoJo. The place is starting to smell..

SHOWGIRLS

Ohhhhh!

Showgirls move up center and surround Trish.

PRISSY

Where'd you get them pearls?

SHOWGIRLS

Dime store imitation.

TRISH

The only imitation is that cheap cologne you're wearing.

SHOWGIRLS

OHHHHH!

NELLY

You sure a bold one coming in here!

TRISH

Where my man goes…I follow.

NELLY

Yeah? Well, your man is a sore loser.

TRISH

At least he's mine. Word has it, yours is up for grabs!

Nelly grabs Trish by the hair and they begin to fight.

SHOWGIRLS

Get her, Nelly!

JOHNNY

Nelly! Leave her be!

EDDIE

Speller Driller! A fresh deck!

SPELLER DRILLER

You boys ready to play some cards?

Everyone surrounds the table to get ready for the game.

JOJO NED

Call it! Come on, Jett, call it!

JOHNNY

No! Have your friend from Detroit call it.

NASTY BOY

I'm from Buc Town. There's a difference.

JOHNNY

In what? Having no class?

NASTY BOY

Heah! I'll take you out right here.

JOJO NED

Chill out, Nasty. I got to get my money first.

EDDIE

One of you boys do something. I got money on this game.

NASTY BOY

Alright I'll call it….Black…No lets play a real game.

The Crowd makes a haunting move forward calling out:

CROWD

Spellbinder!

JOJO NED

'Yeah Spellbinder! Cause I know this dummie can't spell.

JOEY

Who is taking the first round?

TRISH

(*To JoJo*) It's got to be you, baby.

Speller Driller shuffles the deck, picks up the first card and calls out:

SPELLER DRILLER

Antipathy.

EDDIE

Take it, JoJo!

JOJO NED

Antipathy. Antipathy.

EDDIE
Spell the word!

JOJO NED
(*Looking at Trish*) AN..T…IP..A…THY!

CROWD
Go!

JOJO NED
Thought you had me last night didn't you?

NASTY BOY
Nobody's gonna' mess with JoJo tonight!

SPELLER DRILLER
Ready, Johnny?

JOHNNY
Deal!

Speller Driller does a fancy shuffle of the cards.

SPELLER DRILLER
(*Reading the card*) STRATOCUMULUS!!!

The Asante Princess, Ella, and her Royal Sisters, Carrie and Liza, enter with the Ancestral Spirits.

JOHNNY
Stratocumulus. Stratocumulus. Beautiful. You look so Beautiful!!

NASTY BOY
What's with this chump?

JOJO NED
The word was Stratocumulus!

TRISH
He heard the word, he just can't spell it! The dummie!

EDDIE
Spell the word you drew, Jett!

JOHNNY
What was the word?

CROWD
STRATOCUMULUS!

JOHNNY
S T R A T O C U M U L U S!

CROWD
Way to go Johnny!

EDDIE

Bring Jett a drink! On the house!!!

JOHNNY

I don't want anything to drink!

Johnny gets up and crosses to Ella.

JOHNNY

Got something else on my mind.

CROWD

Get the game on your mind!

JOJO NED

We got a score to settle!

JOHNNY

Chill out!

NASTY BOY

I'll chill you out for real.

The Ancestors raise their staffs and everyone in the club, except Johnny, is stilled.

JOHNNY

I'm Johnny….Johnny Jett. Where are you from?

ELLA

The Ancestors say that I am from the Asante of West Africa.

JOHNNY

The Ancestors?

ELLA

My spirit guides.

JOHNNY

Asante …Princess…of Harlem!!

Ancestors raise their staff; Johnny and everyone in club begin to move in syncopated gestures.

Drummers, Elders, African women carrying large bowls on their heads enter. Johnny's consciousness now assumes the nobility of the Yoruba of Benin City. The crowd din the club is stilled.

ASANTEMENA

Your royal ancestor loved our young Princess. From the Yoruba of Ancient Benin City, he traveled up the coast of West Africa, to Cape Coast in Ghana.

JOHNNY

(As his Royal Ancestor) Asante! Your princess lys in chains inside Elmina Castle!

ELLA

Go back to your people.

JOHNNY

The English sail for America in one day.

ELLA

Go! The Slavers will come for you! Canons surround
the castle, tomorrow in the women's quarters, we sail for America.

JOHNNY

Where is the talking drum of the Asante?

ELLA

Do not speak my name!

JOHNNY

I tear my heart out here, in the land of Asante.

Johnny falls to his knees, unconscious.

ELLA

Is he dead?

ASANTEMENA

His spirit has been dead for two hundred years.

ELLA

What does it mean?

ASANTIHENA

The unraveling of hidden mysteries begins.

ELLA

And these people..can they see you?

ANCESTORS

Only those with spirit can see the Ancestors!

They raise their staffs and the crowd comes back to life.

TRISH

He's stalling over there, JoJo. You boys got him scared.

JOJO NED

What a cheat! Look at him! We're on the third round and he's over there making kissy-face
with a dame!

TRISH

And making a fool out of that dame! *(Points to Nelly)*

NELLY

He won't be for long! Nobody cheats on Nelly Bly! *(Stomps out of the room)*

JOEY

Bad nights a comin'. Feel it in my bones.

JOJO NED

Thought you ran a clean house Diamond.

LOUIE

My boss ain't no cheat.

TRISH

Well now, somebody around here is smelling like skunk.

EDDIE

Louie…get this game going!

LOUIE

You got a game to finish, Jett!

JOHNNY

I don't need you to tell me that.

LOUIE

Consider this a friendly reminder…FINISH THE GAME!

JOHNNY

Don't come any closer…I have a princess on my arm!

Johnny walks with Ella to the table.

EDDIE

Speller Driller! Give them the third round!

SPELLER DRILLER

(Shuffles and pulls out the card) SKYSCRAPER!

JOHNNY

Skyscraper! That ain't hard enough for no third round.

SPELLER DRILLER

That's what he drew, Johnny.

JOJO NED

And now I'm gonna spell it.

(Rhyme/Rap)
BUT FIRST ID LIKE TO SAY
TO EVERYONE IN THE HOUSE
WHO CAN REALLY SPELL?
THE MAN OR THE MOUSE
I LOOK IN HIS EYES
I CAN SEE THE FRIGHT
CAUSE WAY DOWN DEEP
HE KNOWS IT GOTS TO BE
JO JO NED TONIGHT!
(Dancing) S…K…Y

The Showgirls imitate JoJo Ned.

SHOWGIRLS
S..K..Y

JOJO NED
S..C..R

SHOWGIRLS
S..C..R

JOJO NED
A..P

SHOWGIRLS
A..P

JOJO NED
ER!

SHOWGIRLS
ER!

EDDIE
It's JoJo Ned's game!

TRISH
Didn't I tell you my man could spell?

CROWD
Hard to beat!

EDDIE
My money was on Ned! Pay up, Jett!

Mrs. Cinder comes running in.

MRS. CINDER
Where are my girls?

JOEY
Disappeared before the show!

MRS. CINDER
Something happened to my girls!

Mrs. Cinder faints and falls to the floor.

ELLA/CARRIE
Mama!

CROWD
It's the Cinder girls!

NELLY
(*Rushing in*) MOVE OUT OF MY WAY! ALL OF YOU!

ELLA

Call a doctor!

CARRIE

It's her heart!

NELLY

Look at the rag muffin! All gussied up!

ELLA

Please, Nelly! My Mama is hurting…bad!

MRS. CINDER

It's all right, baby. I am going on up to heaven with your Daddy.

CARRIE

Don't say that, Mama!

ELLA

Ancestors! Can you help our Mama?

ANCESTORS

What time is it?

ELLA

What time is it somebody?

CROWD

11:59.

ASANTEHENA

One minute to midnight!

ASANTIMENA

Stop the clock!

They raise their staffs and the crowd is motionless.

ASANTEHENA

Harlem does not need a tale of sorrow in the early dawn of tomorrow.

ASANTIMENA

What Harlem needs is a modern song!

ASANTEHENA/ASATIMENA

1930!

(Crowd moves in a syncopated gesture)
1940!

(Crowd moves in a syncopated gesture)
1950!

(Crowd moves in a syncopated gesture)
1960!

(Crowd moves in a syncopated gesture)
1970!

(Crowd moves in a syncopated gesture)
1980!

(Crowd moves in a syncopated gesture)
1990!

(Crowd moves in a syncopated gesture)
The 21st Century!
That should do it!

Modern music comes up. Crowd performs a dance.

EDDIE

Games over and the shows closed. Clear the house, boys.

JOJO NED

We'll look you up next time we in Harlem.

NASTY BOY

Maybe you can learn to spell by then…chump!

EDDIE

You boys come back anytime…and bring the lady!

JOJO NED

Don't even think about it, Diamond.

JoJo Ned, Trish, and Nasty Boy leave.

EDDIE

Ole lady! What you still doing here?

MRS. CINDER

I ain't leaving without my girls.

EDDIE

Well take 'em then. Nelly baby…you look like you could use some company.

NELLY

Guess I could, Mr. Diamond.

EDDIE

What you say we step out for a little after hour entertainment.

NELLY

Do you mean it ,Eddie?

EDDIE

Just said it, didn't I?

LACEY/PRISSY

But, Eddie!

EDDIE
Give Nelly a break, gals! There's plenty of me to go around.

LACEY
Why you two timing double talker!

PRISSY
Two Timing! Three timing trickster!

EDDIE
Ohhhhhh! That hurt!

The Showgirls stomp off to their dressing rooms. Eddie puts Nelly on his arm and they walk out.

There is a moment of silence as Johnny looks around, unable to see Ella.

JOHNNY
Ella! Where did you go?

ELLA
Johnny! I am standing right here!

ASANTIHENA
He can no longer see you.

JOHNNY
Don't disappear on me, girl!

ELLA
Johnny! I am right here.

ASANTIMENA
He can't hear you!

MRS. CINDER
It's you! The African Spirits! I can see you now.

ASANTEHENA/ASANTIMENA
Beloved Mother.

MRS. CINDER
You is talking to me!

ASANTEHENA/ASANTIMENA
Yes, Beloved Mother.

MRS. CINDER
What you want with my girls and me?

ASANTEHENA
To have you know yourself.

MRS. CINDER
What that mean?

ASANTIMENA

To know your own mystery,

ASANTIHENA

Asante in Harlem must use their royal ancestry.

ELLA

I understand you royal ancestors. You want us to use our own knowledge, right here in Harlem.

ASANTIMENA

A true Asante Princess serves her community.

ASANTEHENA

Daughters of Asante! Can you understand this?

ELLA/CARRIE

Yes, Ancestors.

ASANTEHENA/ASANTIMENA

It shall be!

MRS. CINDER

I always knew my girls was beautiful. Don't matter if they was scrubbing floors or cleaning tables, I know the Lord blessed me with three beautiful girls. My only dream is …

LIZA

(*Finishes Mrs. Cinder's thought*)…things working out for us!

CINDER WOMEN

LIZA!!!

The Cinder women hug Liza.

MRS. CINDER

My baby can speak!

LIZA

Come on, Mama…let's go home.

The Cinder family and the Ancestors leave.

Johnny raises his head as Joey pushes his chair out.

JOEY

Come on Johnny. I gots to lock up.

Joey goes downstairs.

JOHNNY

Where's Ella?

ELLA

Right here, Johnny.

JOHNNY

You came back to me?

ELLA

I never left.

JOHNNY

What happened tonight?

ELLA

We found out some things to help us grow here in Harlem.

JOHNNY

I lost the game!

ELLA

But you won my heart.

JOHNNY

Even when you were in rags, you were always my princess.

Johnny bends down and kisses Ella. Music of the 1930's comes up.

Johnny and Ella slow dance.

JOHNNY

Come on, baby…I'll walk you home.

Johnny and Ella leave the club. Joey returns.

JOEY

(Directly to the audience) Johnny Jett lost the card game but found an Asante Princess, right here in Harlem. Good night, folks!

Joey takes off his apron and walks out as soft jazz turns to African drumming.

Fade to Black

End of Play

Beecher Community School District Student actors featured in photographs

Ida B. 'n The Lynching Tree
Michelle Miller
Floyd Carter, Jr.
Gregory Price
Darnel Carr
Nicole Morris
Roger Johnson
Deandre Pitts
Kelli Ford
Clinton McDaniel
Estelle Gusenjow

Mean Molly
Michelle Miller
Deandre Pitts
Micah Scott
Shareka Johnson
Tamika Brown

Let Thy Last Word Be Freedom
Tony Towns
James Fields
Quaendel Warner
Terrence Robinson
Kerry Dantzler
Jenee Price
Dia Price
Daniel Pastorino
Teri Beaugard
Candace Moore
Aaron Higginbottom

Asante
Dia Price
Jenee Price
Quantasia Graham
Kuniko Graham
James Peacock
Matthew Neal
Curtis Parsons
Hermann Byrd
Deondra Hasan
India Fisher